Maġdala

The Lost Story
of Mary Magdalene

Magdala

BRIDGET ERICA

Hopscotch Studio
PO BOX 491
Suite B01294
Kellyville, NSW, 2155
Australia

Publisher's Note: This is a work of fiction. Names, characters,
places, and incidents are a product of the author's imagination All
incidents and dialogue, and all characters, with the exception of
some well-known historical figures, are products of the author's
imagination and are not to be construed as real. Where real-life
historical figures appear, the situations, incidents, and dialogues
concerning those persons are entirely fictional and are not intended
to depict actual events or to change the entirely fictional nature
of the work. In all other respects, any resemblance to actual
persons, living or dead, events, or locales is entirely coincidental.

Magdala/ Bridget Erica. — 1st ed.

ISBN 978-0-6454761-1-8

ACKNOWLEDGEMENTS

I'd like to express my deepest thanks and gratitude to the talented Australian artist, Jennifer Taranto, for her beautiful cover artwork of Mary Magdalene and her incredible support and generosity throughout my journey to publish *Magdala*.

My dedicated and supportive husband Edoardo, for his unfailing belief in me and this novel, whom without I would not have been able to accomplish. Thank you for always giving me the time and space, to nurture and write *Magdala*, while always being my endless sounding board.

And finally, to you, the reader. For choosing to take the time to read these pages and give new life to one the of the greatest women in our history, Mary Magdalene. May she be a source of light, hope, love, inspiration, and healing.

CONTENTS

Acknowledgements

v

From the Author

xi

PREFACE

The Word of Mariamne and the Truth Revealed

xxiii

CHAPTER ONE

My Name is Mariamne

1

CHAPTER TWO

The Condemnation of Innocence

9

CHAPTER THREE

A Blind Woman Sees the Light

19

CHAPTER FOUR

Sealed With a Kiss

33

CHAPTER FIVE

A Secret Ceremony

45

CHAPTER SIX

Prophecy From the Prophet

55

CHAPTER SEVEN

The Last Supper

63

CHAPTER EIGHT

Good Friday

73

CHAPTER NINE

Herbs and Oils

83

CHAPTER TEN

On the Third Day the Son He Rose

89

CHAPTER ELEVEN

The Reckoning

95

CHAPTER TWELVE

The Escape

101

CHAPTER THIRTEEN

Arrival in Alexandria

109

CHAPTER FOURTEEN

The Great Library

117

CHAPTER FIFTEEN

A Dinner With Kings

129

CHAPTER SIXTEEN

A Story in Exchange for Safety

139

CHAPTER SEVENTEEN

The Midnight Escape

145

CHAPTER EIGHTEEN

A Storm and a Birth

155

CHAPTER NINETEEN

Salvation

165

CHAPTER TWENTY

The New Church

173

EPILOGUE

The Final Word

181

Bibliography

183

About the Author

185

About the Artist

187

FOREWORD

From the Author

THE HOLY BIBLE, with all its versions and translations, is probably the most published and revered book in all of history. However, have you ever really reflected on the fact that the entire book — every single chapter, every single story — has been written and edited by a man? Over 2,000 years of history and not a single verse, recollection, or even a word comes from a woman. It doesn't even include a female point of view.

You may say to yourself that women didn't put pen to paper back then, though that isn't entirely true. History has been changed and distorted to make us believe that women were not writers; but in truth, it's believed that the world's first known author was actually a female.

Enheduanna lived during the time of ancient Mesopotamia, dating back to 2285 BCE — more than 2,000 years before the birth of Christ. And yet, though she's a remarkable historical figure, few of us know her name.

As the world's first recognized writer and poet, Enheduanna was widely considered a "triple threat"; a proud princess, priestess, and poet. Her wisdom, compassion, insight, talent, and voice were both feared and revered during her time; but even with all that she accomplished, did our teachers or history textbooks tell us about her or share her story with us? No. Instead, her truth, and she herself, became forgotten, hidden from us.

Women's identities, thoughts, opinions, and actions have been transformed and erased from history for too long, and I believe it's time to correct the record once and for all. We must start to listen and learn not only from *her* story, but from all the strong women who have come before us.

This book is therefore the result of my life's quest and passion to uncover the truth about one of the most important female characters in biblical history. To find out why we have never been told *her* story. And so, with this novel, I pride myself in revealing the true essence of Mary Magdalene's life: all that she was, all that she witnessed and how she viewed the world. With this book, I am raising her from the dead, giving her back her voice, and showering light on her untold and often misconstrued story.

Perhaps, through the reflections and observations of a female, we can better understand history and grasp deeper spiritual secrets and meanings.

Perhaps the female version of the very same stories we've already heard will be completely different, with distinctive understandings, opinions and insights.

Imagine what we can learn from that female perspective.

Imagine how that perspective might have changed history, if it had been taught to us, or if we'd listened to it?

As a young girl growing up within the Catholic Church and attending a Catholic school, I remember having such strong insights into the religion I was supposedly being taught. Often, I felt so confused as to why the adults and priests didn't seem to really understand the scriptures they were teaching us. I was even more baffled as to why they believed that Jesus would return again; why they believed, after 2,000 years, that we were still waiting for His physical return. For me, it was obvious, even then, that His death and "resurrection" were His final chapter. It was clear to me that the entire purpose of His life was that He lived as a man, a true man, who showed us how richly and deeply we can lead our own lives, just as He lived His.

I have a clear memory of being at a school mass when I was about nine years old. The priest was addressing the staff and students, and asked, "Where is Jesus and when will He return?" Looking back, I know it was probably a rhetorical question, but at nine years old, I didn't know what a rhetorical question was, so I boldly stood up in front of the entire school — 800 pupils, plus teachers — and said: "Jesus lives in each and every one of us. He lives in our hearts. We don't need to wait for His physical return, as He is already alive in each and every one of us."

For me, even at nine years old, the question was absurd because the answer was so clear. Why didn't everyone already know this and why were we continually told this unrealistic story of the physical resurrection? Men don't rise from the dead — and Jesus had to be a man, for if He was simply divine, there is no point to His entire story. Jesus being purely divine only works to separate us from Him, but Jesus being a simple man works to unify us with both Him and the Divine. Therefore, Jesus had to live a mortal life, completely and fully as a man, so He could best unite us with God.

My hunger to expose the truth of the Christian theology only grew stronger and stronger as I reached my late teens and early twenties. When I learnt about them, I immersed myself in the Dead Sea Scrolls (also known as the Nag Hammadi texts), which are a collection of ancient scrolls and writings that were uncovered in Egypt in 1945. They're considered to be the earliest writings and recordings of Jesus's life, and many people believe the Gospel of Thomas may have actually preserved the true words of Jesus.

I purchased as many copies and translations of the texts as I could find. I read historians' and theologians' points of view on both the texts and the Christian religion in general. I wanted to know everything. As I went through all of my research and reading, something started to stir within me. I could feel that something was still missing for me, and it was hinted at in the Gospel of Philip. After reading this gospel for the first time, I started to make sense of all the original gospels and biblical stories. I realized that I wanted to discover more about Mary Magdalene, that I wanted to know her story and learn from her. I couldn't accept that the Church Fathers had simply turned Mary, the mother of Jesus, into a virgin, and Mary Magdalene, an unknown woman, into a prostitute and a sinner. It just seemed too simplistic — an obvious manipulation of the truth.

What was it about these women and their lives that made the Church Fathers erase their stories and make over their identities? What were they so afraid of? I wondered.

So, I began reading books about Mary Magdalene, hunting for her story in whatever I could find. But my appetite to learn of her essence, her knowledge and deep understanding of Jesus, was always left unsatisfied. The books I found were either hypothetical, historical points of views on her possible life (completely missing the point of all the mystery and her spiritual journey), or ambiguously Gnostic and filled with incredibly difficult-to-grasp concepts.

After a decade of searching, I finally surrendered and accepted that the book I was looking for did not exist. And so, it became my mission to write it myself. I did so by tapping into my inner child, who had such a strong connection with and insight into Jesus's life and His true message, and aligning myself with the young, ambitious and deeply spiritual female I am.

Completing this book has taken me more than eleven years, with a large part of that time spent in Rome. Along the way, I've also traversed my own journey of healing, becoming a Reiki Master Teacher, opening two clinics in Australia, founding the Australian Centre for Clinical Reiki and teaching Reiki healing to hundreds of pupils.

It was through my journey to become a healer that I learnt how to reconnect with Mary Magdalene, and fully understand *her* role as a healer. Ultimately, after more than a decade of interest in Mary, the eight years of learning and growing I embarked on in order to practice Reiki healings, was what helped the final chapters of this book come to me. It was then that I felt as though Mary's story was revealed.

My own personal journey as a healer has taught me about life, our bodies, our souls and our connection or disconnection to God and the Divine. As I healer, my primary role is to reconnect people with their higher selves, with their higher purposes, and with God, or the Divine, or Source (or however one best connects with the terminology). I am simply a witness and a vessel who channels this space and healing — the rest unfolds with ease and grace. I call this the grace of God.

These things together — my research, my spiritual

journey, my quest to discover Mary Magdalene's story — have culminated in this, my gift to every woman who has been searching for the truth.

It is so very unfortunate that powerful men of the past re-wrote Mary's story, erasing her as much as possible from our records. I truly believe this was because of who Mary Magdalene was and what she stood for. Her in-depth wisdom, actions and knowledge threatened their fragile systems, their perceived paths to power and glory. It saddens me that women over the centuries have not had access to her teachings, or even had a knowledge of who she really was. Modern women of so many different cultures and faiths have been failed. They have been robbed of a true female role model, one who stood up against the evil undercurrents of a heavily patriarchal world.

I ask you now to take a moment to reflect and ask yourself: What would it mean if Mary Magdalene was a disciple of Jesus? If Mary Magdalene was the wife of Jesus? How would the history of the world be different if Mary Magdalene's stories, her gospels and the other Nag Hammadi texts had always been available to us? If they were researched and talked about?

There is a stunning and miraculous reason why the Dead Sea Scrolls and Nag Hammadi texts were kept hidden and safe for almost 2,000 years. They were protected from harm and only revealed when the time came that they would not be destroyed or hidden from the public. This, I believe, is a true miracle gifted to us by Mary Magdalene. She protected the truth for so many years, so that, finally, when they were discovered in 1945, they were authenticated and published so that we can learn from her; rediscover her; honour her.

Now, ask yourself: What if we always knew that empathy and intuition would allow us to understand the true teachings of Jesus, in the same way that Mary Magdalene did? What if we had always known of Mary Magdalene's enemies and of how Peter, and the men who followed him, were coming from a place of fear and jealousy when they destroyed her story? What if Mary Magdalene was just another disciple who was, at one point, treated the same as the men? What if she lived as an example of how a woman of insight and faith can be just as worthy as a male?

What if the women of our past, 1,000 years ago, and even 100 years ago, always had a strong female archetype to follow? One who could inspire them, empower them. How might our history have changed?

Now ask yourself why Mary Magdalene's honourable cause, miracles, healings and teachings were tainted by men calling her a prostitute and a sinner? Why do you think there are only two female role models in Christian history: the Virgin and the Whore? Just as Jesus insisted on being called the Son of Man, maybe it's time that we too insist on calling these women, and other lost women of history, by their true titles.

Do you have the courage to question our Church Fathers? To question the history we have been told and to say with a loud voice that these men were wrong? Do you have the intelligence and patience to re-examine the holy texts and traditions with new eyes? To read between the lines and recognize how those who changed the meaning of a word here and there have worked to separate us from God?

The texts were designed to guide us towards the light. But slowly, century after century, men in purple robes have manipulated these writings, and the events they described, so that women were robbed of the truth, keeping us powerless and controllable.

Do you have the ability to, once and for all, set aside fears and discrimination, sexism and racism so we can finally reclaim one of the most important female role models in the history of man and woman? To find out who the true Mary Magdalene was and what can we learn from her?

I invite you to bring Mary Magdalene back into your life, and to teach your daughters, your sisters, your granddaughters, and all the women in your life her lessons.

May the story of Mary Magdalene and who she was allow us to honour her while also setting us free.

* * *

I am the Beginning and the End.

I am honored and scorned.

I am the prostitute and the saint.

I am married and a maiden.

I am the mother and the daughter.

I am the limbs of my mother.

I am barren

and my children are many.

I am she who married magnificently,

and I have no husband.

I am the one who brings children and I do

not bear children.

I am the consolation of labor pains.

I am the bride and the bridegroom,

and my husband brought me forth.

I am my father's mother

and my husband's sister,

and he is my child.

I am the incomprehensible silence
and the idea often brought to mind.

I am the voice sounding throughout the world
and the word appearing everywhere.

I am the sounding of my name,
For I am knowledge and ignorance.

I am shame and bravery.

I am without shame; I am full of shame.

I am power and I am trepidation.

I am conflict and peace.

Listen to me,

For I am the scandalous and magnificent one.

— Excerpted from the Nag Hammadi Library, a collection
   which was unearthed in 1945; this selection is taken from
   the Gnostic poem, The Thunder, Perfect Mind[1]

---

1   https://92d8dda75447112de0c1-0e939f13a06bd1dbeb5309286eaa14e5.ssl.cf5.
    rackcdn.com/ws_01_hymn_isis.pdf

The Word of Mariamne and the Truth Revealed

FOR MORE THAN 2,000 YEARS my name has been printed in the holy book and buildings have been erected in my honour. At the same time, men in ornate robes have trampled on my words, tainted my name and hidden my story from you. The exceptional events of my life have been erased and lost like pebbles thrown into the deep, murky waters of a bottomless pond. Many have called me a prostitute and a sinner. Many have sat back on their thrones, sipped their wine and made you believe that my name is unclean.

May the truth be known that I am, and always have been, a woman, a daughter, a sister, a wife, a lover, a healer and a mother. A woman who was never afraid to live with her heart or speak with the truth. One who never weakened in the face of oppression. My name is Mariamne, I was born in Magdala, I am the sister of Philip, the daughter of Jonas, and the wife of Yeshua. This is my story.

CHAPTER ONE

My Name is Mariamne

*32: There were three who always walked with the Lord: Mary,
his mother; the sister of his mother; and Miriam of Magdala, known as his companion; for him, Miriam is a sister, a
mother, and a wife.[2]*

— GOSPEL OF PHILIP

AT THE EARLY AGE OF 12, I left my family and moved from
my hometown in Magdala to live with my aunties in Jerusalem. The women in my family had long worked with
plants and oils, a practice that went back to the oldest
of our grandmothers that time could remember. According to family tradition, each firstborn daughter would be
sent to Jerusalem to learn our people's ancient craft once
she had started her monthly moon cycle. She would cut

---

2   The Gospel of Philip, Page 61, Plate 107, Translated by Jean-Yves Leloup,
Inner Traditions 2004, p.65.

all ties with her parents, cousins and siblings, and dedicate her time to learning from and serving her elders. After three years of tutelage in ancient techniques and secret remedies, she would return to society and use her skills to heal the sick and cure ailments of the heart.

Therefore, with the blood blessing of my first menstruation at the age of 12, it was my duty and destiny to leave my childhood behind me and continue my familial legacy. Despite all that it meant for me, it was an honour to learn the craft, and I was eager to begin.

I packed a small sack with my finest robes and a handful of letters and drawings my sisters had prepared for me. My mother gifted me fruits, grains and colourful wildflowers gathered in a beautiful woven basket that she had been weaving over the previous months, though I had not known she was preparing it as my parting gift. When it was time to leave, she embraced me firmly, and I observed tears in her eyes as she handed me over to my older brother Marcus, who would accompany me on my journey to Jerusalem.

I was grateful for the beautiful gift from my mother and promised to use it every day on my trips to the market and when I was attending healing ceremonies. Though I was young, I was not sad to leave. I had been waiting for that day my entire life, and I welcomed the adventure.

As children, my mother would tell us magical stories about my aunties, what special powers they had and what they could do with them. My younger sisters and cousins were envious of the fact that I was chosen to go, but they lined the streets to bid me farewell, grinning with happiness for me, as I waved them goodbye, blowing kisses in their direction.

The journey to Jerusalem seemed to glide by as I fantasised about what lay ahead for me. Meeting my aunties for the first time gave me such a thrill — they were just as my mother had described them to me, and were true angels.

The aunties quickly took me under their wings and taught me all their secrets. Of course, their lessons were not without arguments, as there were always one or two aunties who insisted their methods were superior to the others. But there was also the sweet one who brought me special treats from the market and organised special deliveries to my sisters and cousins in Magdala. And, though I was not supposed to remain in contact with them, I often sent my sisters and cousins letters and gifts from Jerusalem.

Like my mother had done with me, I'd share stories of the magical remedies and miraculous cures we were creating. The girls would often send requests for love potions, so I would secretly prepare musk and lavender oil and send it to them with a prayer that they would find their perfect husband. One who would protect them, provide for them and love them selflessly.

The first months of living with my aunties was such a wondrous experience. They seemed like magical beings, like angels who walked the earth, and at times I didn't feel like I was good enough to be one of them. Of course, it was difficult to be so far away from my parents and siblings, but as I spent more and more time with my aunties, a hunger to learn and spread the light of my ancestors grew inside of me.

My aunties were the strongest and bravest women I had ever known. They taught me how to grow and cultivate many species of plants and herbs. I learned how to dry the leaves and create potions or extract their sweet oils. But above all, they taught me how to be a woman and how to stand on my own. I embraced their wisdom and I skillfully learned how to continue my daily activities in a city filled with lies, thieves and masculine-governed laws.

Though it had initially been a surprise to me, I grew used to being spat on by men when buying ingredients at the markets. I learnt that I was considered a disgrace, for it was customary that a woman would work only for her husband and family. I was not married, though nor did I have patience for rules that tried to limit me. I was a healer and I determined that their petty laws would not stop me from living my life and helping those in need. I was born with a gift and a duty. I knew that if God had chosen to endow me with such a gift, I was obliged to share it with whomever needed it.

During this time, Jerusalem was ruled by King Herod and the Roman Empire. The local Jewish laws prevented married women from being touched or treated by male doctors, and so these women would come to us for healings. Often, they would bring their children and unmarried daughters as well, for they felt safer in our care.

Our cures were well known amongst most women of our village, though we managed to maintain a low public profile by only treating women when they were menstruating. You see, Jewish traditions considered women to be unclean during their cycle, and they were barred from entering a Temple during this time. So, when the men attended Temple, the menstruating women would come to us. As long as this tradition was upheld, our treatments were received without men's knowledge, saving us from public persecution.

My aunties also believed that when a woman has her menstrual flow, her body and soul are aligned with the moon, which allows the healings to transition more quickly and have a greater effect. They believed that if a woman's cycle is out of sync with the moon cycle, she must reconnect with her heart and body and address the issues in her life that are preventing her from being her authentic self. My aunt Rebekah, one of the oldest and sweetest of them all, would explain it to me by saying:

"Like the stars that help the lost traveller find his way home during the darkest of the nights, the moon is every woman's guide. And it is the light that stirs within our hearts that gives us access to the essence of life. When these two elements are aligned, miracles can, and do, happen."

I adored listening to Rebekah, as she had a way with words that made her prayers stick to the hairs of your skin and penetrate deep within your soul. She would snuggle next to me at night and tell me stories; she would stroke my hair and show me warm affection. In her comforting embrace I always felt loved and at home. She became a second mother to me and I, perhaps, became the daughter she never had.

Much like the Vestal Virgins, who often came to us for healings and to learn sacred rituals, the healers in my family would take a vow of celibacy and remain virgins for our entire lives. Each month we would come together in secret to celebrate a deeper insight into the mysteries of the universe and to incarnate the divine feminine spirit.

As women, we celebrated our natural connection to the Divine. We came together to help each other discover and grow our own unique healing powers, while also sharing the great wisdoms and lessons that had been handed down to us.

Our circle would often serve as a healing space for whomever of us was in need of individual healing. Each of us had days that we needed to come to the circle and ask our sisters for help. Often, these healing requests would occur after an act of violence or rage was perpetrated against us, something that was common as we performed our daily activities in town. The men of Jerusalem could be cruel, and harboured a deep lust for the Vestal Virgins that often manifested in horrendous actions against women's wills and their holy right to protection.

So too were my aunties and myself often targeted for our virginal innocence and purity. What is it about men that makes them want to take, so violently and arrogantly, what is not theirs to have? It is as if something dark and evil stirs within them, driving them to act on their deviant impulses. It is like they feel a poisonous desire to consume and possess all that is pure and sweet, tainting the world around us and robbing the light from within us.

Thankfully, we had our sacred circle to help us heal; it protected us from these dark and deep-seated energies that occupied the minds and lustings of the men around us. Most often, we would leave our gatherings feeling nurtured, light, calm, reinvigorated and reborn. These circles allowed us to continue our path of healing and offerings, for if we were tainted or in need of healing ourselves, we could not serve those around us. We knew the importance of looking after ourselves, our bodies, our minds and our energy, so that we could give the very best of ourselves to our healings. Our circles served many purposes, but perhaps most importantly, they helped maintain our daily wellbeing, balance and harmony. I will be forever grateful for this, and for those remarkable women, for whom I would have given my life.

CHAPTER TWO

The Condemnation of Innocence

WHILE IT MAY ALREADY BE apparent that my life was not an ordinary one, things took a dramatic turn for me one specific morning on the seventh day of Spring. I had been living in Jerusalem for nine years by that point and had become skillful at working my way around town. I knew who sold the freshest herbs, which women would try to steal my secrets so they could sell them to the Jewish High Priests, and the men with whom it worked best to act charming and demure.

That particular morning, I awoke at sunrise and made my way towards the marketplace. It was earlier than usual, but I had no time to waste; I needed to trade some spices for a cure I was working on that would help save a very sick child.

I had barely arrived when the streets erupted in shouting and disarray. As I looked up to locate the source of the commotion, a young girl came running straight into my arms. She clasped her hands onto me firmly, shaking and begging for my help. I was shocked to see that her face was dripping with blood and her clothes were torn, and then horrified to hear from her that though she was no older than thirteen years, a group of men wanted her dead.

I dropped my basket, clenched her hands and held her behind me. My heart pounded but I did not doubt it was the right thing to protect her. I closed my eyes and concentrated on my breathing. Though my heart felt as though it would jump from my throat, I could feel that my feet were solid on the ground and my spirit was filled with light. I allowed my breath to slowly calm my body; I invited the light to become me; and when I finally opened my eyes, I discovered that I was surrounded by a group of men who carried sticks in their hands. Still, I used my concentration to block out their yelling, their threats, and I stood solid. I stood strong.

Nothing, certainly no mere man, was going to make me move. One by one, I looked each man in the eye, held their gaze and stood my ground. Time felt endless, though I suspect no more than a few moments had passed. Then, gradually, the men seemed to run out of words. The determination, the hate, dissipated from their eyes, and they eventually turned and ambled away, leaving the girl trembling in my arms.

I brought the girl to my home, bathed her, fed her and told her stories about lands far away that were inhabited by angels no bigger than my hand. I stroked her hair and told her how they lived in the forests and danced on the flower tops, drinking glasses filled with liquid gold and living a life of magic.

After some time, I learnt that her name was Sara, and, after her tears had slowed, she told me how her uncle had violated her. She explained that though she was promised to wed in ten days, she hadn't been able to hide her swollen belly behind loose clothes any longer. When her father had realized that she was with child, she'd refused to disgrace the family name by telling him the truth about what her uncle had done. And so, believing that his daughter had lain with another man, her father had decried that, in keeping with the law of the people, she would be stoned to death.

That night Sara slept peacefully in my arms like the innocent child she was, but when morning broke my protection was no longer enough to save her from the darkness that stirred within the townsfolk.

At the break of dawn, my house filled with seven men who dragged Sara and myself to the centre of the village. One of the men must have struck me unconscious, as I do not remember what happened next. When I awoke it was high morning and the two of us were surrounded by a crowd of raging men. Words were flying out of their mouths like weapons meant to hit and hurt us. Lies of prostitution, demons and madness polluted the air. When I used all my strength to sit up, I recognized the truth of what was happening: the men were holding stones in their hands — I was soon to be the subject of a public execution.

I quickly turned to check on Sara, but when I saw her motionless body slumped on the ground behind me, I knew it was too late. Her clothes were stained with blood and it was clear that life had drained from her.

I can only describe what happened next as coming from the shock of it all, but suddenly a wail stirred deep within the pit of my stomach and then came thundering out through my throat. It was as if I had no control of it as it possessed and devoured my entire body. My voice screeched through the dusty streets of Jerusalem and in the echo of my cry the square turned completely silent.

Amidst this silence, my eyes were drawn to a man who stood amongst the crowd. It was clear that he was not like the others when his crystal clear eyes locked into mine. Suddenly, it felt as though time stood still; everything and everyone was frozen around us. Looking into his eyes allowed the harsh reality of the situation to simply melt away. I regained my breath and composure, and a sense of calm came rushing over me. I had never experienced anything quite like it.

His gaze did not stray from mine as he slowly made his way to the centre of the circle. Facing the crowd, and without saying a word, he took a stick from one of the men and drew a line across the sandy road. He then began to speak.

"He who has not sinned, I beg you to come forth and be the first to throw a stone at this woman," yelled the man into the crowd.

"Hear my words and act wisely," he continued. "As only those who have not sinned have the right to come forth and cast their stones."

At that moment the man knelt and bowed his head, as though he waited for the first stone to strike me. I closed my eyes, clasping my hands together, and I waited with him. At first, there was silence, but it was soon broken by the sound of rocks hitting the dusty ground. I wondered whether the men were missing me or if I was being hit but somehow could not feel it. When I gradually gained the courage to open my eyes, I discovered that the men were walking away. The sounds I could hear were from each and every one of them dropping their rocks to the ground as they left the square.

Before me remained the man, head bowed to the ground, still and silent. When the square was finally empty — aside from my aunties, and the sisters of Sara, who rushed to her side and cradled her body before taking her away — the man stood and approached me slowly. He stretched out his hand and beaconed me to rise. Shakily, I grasped his fingers and rose to my feet, in disbelief of what had just happened before us.

The man said, "come with me," at the same time my blessed dear aunties ran towards me, praising the Gods for saving my soul. I wanted to hug my aunties and dissolve into their safe embrace but at the same time I could not draw myself away from this man. I turned to Rebekah, who was trembling and crying with joy as she placed my hands in hers.

"Mariamne, we are here now. Everything will be okay. Come let us take you home," Rebekah beckoned sweetly. I looked blankly into her eyes and it felt as if her words simply washed over me. Without thinking or evaluating the circumstances I replied:

"Rebekah, my angel, thank you for your strength and unconditional belief in me. I know not what has taken place before us today, but something deep inside me says I should go with this man. Trust me please. Go with our sisters and take care of our fallen Sara. Her family needs you all more than me right now. I love you."

With those departing words, Rebekah embraced me with all her strength before reluctantly releasing her hands from around me.

"We love you, Mariamne, and we will always be here for you. Stay safe and may God continue to protect you. Our door is forever open. Come home when you feel ready."

The man stood silently and waited for me to say my goodbyes. Then he turned his shoulder without saying a word and gestured for me to follow him. We walked in silence through the tiny and twisted streets of Jerusalem until we arrived at the door of a modest village dwelling. Two men guarded the door and nodded politely in my direction, as the man invited me into the home.

I followed him through the entrance of the home and it was at this moment that the reality of what had just happened fully struck me. My knees collapsed beneath me and I fell to the ground, sobbing. As the man stood before me, it felt as though every river in the world came pouring out of me. I washed his feet with my tears and I dried them with my hair, for I owed this man my life.

When I had no more tears left to flow and my cheeks had dried, he looked deep into my eyes and said, "No man will ever forget you, as you have come to fulfil your purpose."

That night I slept on the floor at the feet of this man, he who had taken such courage to save my life.

I awoke the next morning to find the house filled with chatter and laughter. A group of men were gathered around my saviour, listening attentively as he spoke. It was only as I quietly entered the room that I realized who the man who had saved me was.

For weeks his name had been mentioned around town, this man from Nazareth who could bring men back from the dead and cast away evil spirits. He was Yeshua, and though I had longed to meet him, I never could have imagined that we would have an encounter that would change the course of my life forever.

That morning, he spoke about how to be an evolved and authentic person. "This cannot not be achieved by following the laws of the Romans or the Jews," he told us. "But by owning and taking responsibility for who we really are: the sons and daughters of God. All made in His image, for nothing separates us from Him but our own words and actions."

Yeshua's words sang in my heart, stirring something deep within me that made me want to sit and listen to him for eternity.

Looking around the room, I caught sight of a surprising, but familiar face amongst the men. Could it really be my brother, Philip? I made a gesture in his direction and he smiled that big, beautiful, joyful smile that was so familiar to me. He quickly approached me and ushered me into the next room, where we embraced each other like never before. It had been nine years since I'd seen my younger brother, and I could feel that his shoulders were broader and that he had filled out into a strong young man in the years since we'd last been together. It felt so good to hold him in my arms.

"What are you doing here?" I exclaimed. I knew he had a duty to be working with our father in Magdala, and by no means should he have been in Jerusalem. He explained to me that he had heard about this man named Yeshua, and after finding him in Jerusalem, he'd decided to become one of his first followers. Before him were John, Mark, James and Thomas; they called themselves the Apostles of Yeshua.

He explained to me how he had been following me that day in the market when I came across Sara, and how he had wanted to surprise me. He told me about how he was so proud of what I had done for that girl. When he heard that the local men were planning to bring us both to justice, he went to Yeshua for help. Yeshua had told him that all would be well and, as it happens, he had been right.

Filled with joy, I hugged my brother with pure delight. It felt as if we were two children again, free to dream and dance in the fields. Although I knew how disappointed our father would be, I also knew my brother was doing the right thing. It was as if for the first time we were being given hope for a future of freedom and love. As though it was our true calling to become warriors of light in the movement against oppression and slavery.

CHAPTER THREE

A Blind Woman Sees the Light

I REMAINED IN THE COMPANY of my brother and Yeshua – men who made me feel calm and safe — for the following days. I was still shaken from Sara's death and the heinous events that had surrounded it, and a deep sadness lay heavy on my chest.

I could feel that I was carrying the burden of Sara with me, and though I knew I had done everything possible to save her, it felt like her injustice had retreated into silence. Jerusalem was a hostile place, and though her young body, and that of her unborn child, now lay beneath the ground, it didn't seem right that her story and the truth of what had happened to her would go untold. How blind were we, that the murder of a helpless child could bury the truth of the actions of the man who's poisonous desire had devoured her innocence?

A burning rage lingered deep inside of me, and I knew it had the potential to drive me to the streets, to scream as loud as I could about the injustices placed on this poor girl. I knew too that this kind of behaviour would only serve to have me labelled as a mad woman — a sentence that leaves many women to rot as an outcast, consumed by their "madness," and waiting for the day when God would have the mercy to end their suffering and permit their sensitive soul to escape the ever so limited plane of earth. This was not the path I wanted to take, and if I continued to think about it, I knew I would surely go mad.

I had learnt long ago that there was no sense or reason to man's ideologies and practices. I also knew there was little I could do to change those ways. And, so, I'd done what I could in silence, while praying that one day they too would be able to see the light that burned so brightly in all women's souls.

Yeshua could sense my mixed emotions, my sadness and anger, and asked me to join him on a walk to a very particular part of town. Desperate to put my thoughts to rest, I agreed and soon found myself in a place called the Valley of Death. Located on the outskirts of Jerusalem, it was here that many widows, lepers and mad men spent the rest of their days, knee-deep in poverty, filth and starvation.

I was surprised to see that the state of these people did not bother Yeshua. He spoke with each of them using love and compassion, as though they were his very own family members.

Most people would not dare to enter the Valley as it was widely believed that just being there could lead one to catch a disease or be possessed by the demons that were cursed to remain there for eternity, forever searching for a soulless body to inhabit.

The people who lived there represented the greatest fears of mankind and were thus cast out to the Valley of Death, where they were left to fend for themselves in a place where man would no longer have to face the reality of their very own fears.

We continued our journey through the Valley until a blind woman, clothed in black, stretched out her arm and yelled, "STOP!" with such command and authority, we couldn't do anything but comply.

The woman, leaning against an old stick for support, slowly rose to her feet. Her eyes were milky white, and though it was clear she was blind, it felt as though she could see us when she looked directly at Yeshua and started to speak.

"I have waited four years and sixty-five days for you to walk across my path. And now that you have, you must do one thing for me."

"And what would that be?" asked Yeshua.

Reaching forward, she firmly gripped Yeshua's hands in hers and said, "Give me back my sight."

"And why should I do such a thing?" replied Yeshua, smiling at the woman and seemingly welcoming her interaction.

"Because I prayed for you, I knew you would come. You carry the light, I can see it. You also carry the burden of needing to share this light. It is not yours to keep," ranted the woman.

"So, tell me," Yeshua said. "In the four years and sixty-five days that you have passed here waiting for me to come, what have you learnt?"

"I know I am here because I could not forgive my husband for giving our youngest daughter away. He did it so that he could bring food home and feed our other children. The food we ate without her then consumed my sight and I failed to care for my family. I have since learnt that it was not my husband who I needed to forgive but myself for allowing it to happen. I allowed the darkness to enter my body and eat away my sight. I have repented for what happened to my daughter, and I have deserved every moment that has passed before me in this place, but, please, give me back the light so I can see again. So that I can go find her," pleaded the woman.

And with those words Yeshua bent down and gathered dirt from the ground. He placed it in a small jar he had carried with him and poured three small drops of liquid into the jar. He then mixed the contents into a paste before smearing it onto the eyes of the woman.

We stood beside her and watched as she covered her eyes with her hands and began to weep. We continued to watch as her tears began to wash away the dirt.

"Thank you, thank you," the woman wept, as she wiped the remains of the dirt and tears from her eyes.

Standing before us, she slowly opened her eyes, which had gone from milky white to a bright green; they shone with a light that beamed from deep within. She could see, I realized in amazement.

She embraced Yeshua. "It's more beautiful than I remembered," she said.

The woman soaked up the sight of her surroundings, clearly enjoying every inch, colour and impurity that were now hers to witness. Despite the haggard and hardened faces of the people who shared the Valley with her, she drank in the views that surrounded her, the sun as it beamed down from the heavens, and kissed the ground with a soft golden embrace.

We left the woman to enjoy her newfound wisdom and fresh sight as we continued to walk along the path.

Not long after, we stopped in front of a small boy no older than eight years of age. He lay hopeless-looking on the street; his eyes were half closed, and his head was heavy as it lowered towards the ground. His skin was covered in boils and open wounds. He seemed to have completely resigned himself to his ailments — he simply lay there, not even stirring at our presence.

From what I could tell, he was one of many children residing in the Valley due to leprosy. He'd most likely been abandoned by his family, a practice that was all too common when impoverished families could no longer care for their ill children, or when villagers condemned and ostracized those families that did choose to care for their sick children. The end result was the same: families that abandoned the sick and the weak, leaving them to fend for themselves in the Valley of Death.

As we stood before the young boy, Yeshua casually turned to me and said, "Heal him."

"Heal him?" I queried, perplexed.

"Yes, heal him. You're a healer, heal him," insisted Yeshua, gesturing in the small boy's direction.

"I don't have any of my herbs or oils or prayers prepared for him," I replied. "I cannot simply heal him."

Yeshua stared at me openly. By this time a small crowd had started to form around us, and I sincerely had no idea of what to do. I was not prepared in the slightest for this turn of events. I had no inkling how to cure this poor boy. I'd never been in this situation. The last thing I wanted to do was to give him any false hope or belief that I could almost instantly heal the sick as Yeshua had done. My tradition and knowledge in healing were not of the same virtue as his.

Yeshua stood silent in front of me. The small boy opened his big brown eyes and looked straight into mine. He unsteadily rose to his feet and stood, waiting.

I looked at Yeshua, searching his eyes for help. Silently, I pleaded with him to give me some sort of guidance. To show me or tell me what I was meant to do.

Then, in answer to my silent prayer, he leaned in close to me and whispered:

"Place your hands on his shoulders. Listen to him and communicate with him through your heart. You will know what to do."

Although I was unsure, something deep within my being told me to trust him. I took a deep breath and stepped forward. I placed my bare hands onto the boy's shoulders and closed my eyes.

At first, nothing happened. Then, I took a deep breath and focused. I started to breathe the golden light into my heart space and before I knew it a flood of images came rushing towards me. Scenes of children being burnt alive, women running for their lives, crops being burnt, animals slaughtered, murder, blood and sacrifice.

Startled by the violent imagery, I quickly took my hands off the boy and stepped backwards. My heart was pounding and I was out of breath. Yeshua moved forward and placed my hands back on the boy's shoulders. Keeping his hands above mine, he asked me to tell him what I saw.

My voice was shaking as I quietly recounted to Yeshua the shocking images I was seeing. Slowly, Yeshua let go of my hands, looked at me and said:

"Those images are of the past life of this boy. They're of the sins of his fathers. He is carrying with him the burdens of the past and the wrongdoings of his ancestors. In order to break the ties and free his lineage from an eternity of torment and suffering, his soul is bearing the scars of past sins, and they are manifesting on his skin, causing him immense pain and isolation."

Yeshua placed his hand over my heart and continued to enlighten me:

"Talk and listen to him with your heart. You can heal him. Send back that which is not his and heal the void, the pain and emptiness that remain. God will guide you. He is talking to you through your heart and you will know what to do."

Yeshua then stepped back into the crowd. All eyes were on me as I tentatively held this small boy beneath my hands. I closed my eyes and once again breathed through my heart. This time it was as if a bright star had fallen from the night's sky and landed in the centre of my chest. In my mind's eye a bright blue silver light beamed brilliantly outwards and embraced the entire being of the small child. It was in this moment that I knew God was working through me. I was but a conduit for His command.

Without conscious thought, words started to flow from my lips.

"In the name of God the almighty I command that all that is not yours be returned to its original and rightful place. With love and grace, I free you of your burdens, I forgive you of your sins, and the sins of your fathers and forefathers. I lift you up into my hands and I pronounce you healed. So mote it be."

There was a conviction and strength that came from my voice that was distinct from my usual way of communicating. It was as if an entity so much greater and more powerful than myself beamed its immense light and love through me. I could feel that these words caressed every cell of the small boy, not leaving a speck of imperfection in its wake.

I opened my eyes and looked down at the boy. His skin was golden, soft and smooth. Not a single scar, boil or mark was left behind. I could hardly believe my eyes. I had healed this boy with Yeshua as my witness.

I turned to Yeshua, beaming with joy. This small boy could now go back to his village and find his family. He could work and bring abundance and wealth to those who needed it. He was being gifted a second chance at this life and was finally free to leave the hell on earth that had become his home. Destiny had a new vision for him and I prayed that God would continue to protect and nurture him.

Yeshua returned my look with an all-knowing smile and gestured to me that we should continue on our path. My mind was racing, my heart was beaming and I was buzzing with absolute bliss. Was it really that easy to heal? I wondered.

Then, still stunned and in utter disbelief, I shook away my thoughts and calmed my ego, which I could feel rising up and wanting to claim responsibility and praise for what had occurred beneath my hands. I allowed my racing thoughts to drift away as I focused on walking besides Yeshua.

As I forced myself to look into the eyes and faces of all those we passed, I wondered how Yeshua could leave so many suffering and needy people behind? What was it that made him stop and choose someone to help? Were we all not equal in God's eyes and deserving of His clemency?

When I voiced my doubts to Yeshua, he explained that not everyone was ready to be healed; that we all had our soul's path to walk, that some needed more time to learn their lessons, and others, like the blind woman, had chosen this suffering for a reason and needed time to heal themselves.

"You see, it was not I who healed her, but she who healed herself through penance, reflection and understanding," Yeshua counselled. "She had procured her own soul remedy and called me to her when she was ready to see the light. You too will be called upon by the sick, the hungry, the poor and the lonely. You too carry the light, and they will seek you out. Remember this. Those who seek shall find. It is your duty to listen to them, to heal them. You have been called and your time has come. I will guide you as I can; however, your spirit knows different truths than mine and you have the unique ability to embrace and encompass a feminine divinity that will flow freely through you and into those who call your name."

As we were talking, a young lady approached us and placed her hand on my arm. I turned towards her, took in her dull eyes and immediately sensed that her heart carried a heavy sadness.

"I saw what you did with that poor boy. I beg you. Help me. My mind is plagued with darkness. I have not slept in sixteen nights. My heart will not stop racing and I fear I will die at any moment," the woman pleaded.

I turned to Yeshua, and he simply nodded his head, inviting me, in his mysterious way, to help her. This time, without hesitation, I placed my hands on the woman's shoulders as she bowed her head to the ground and knelt before me. The energy I felt as I touched her was calmer and softer than that of the boy. As I closed my eyes, I saw a woman dressed in white walking towards me. She was holding a small bunch of wildflowers and around her neck hung a simple chain with a clear crystal jar. My focus was immediately drawn to the blue-light liquid that shone and softly swished around the jar. In my mind's eye I asked the lady who she was and what it was she carried with her. She told me she was the woman's mother; in her hands she carried the flowers her daughter had left beside her lifeless body and the jar contained every teardrop that had fallen from her daughter's eyes since her mother's death.

"Please tell her she will not die like me," the mother begged. "She does not have my illness and the darkness in her mind is of her own creation. I beg you, tell her she is free. I have left this plane so that she can be free. It is not God's plan for her to be here with me. Her family is waiting for her. She will be safe. She will not die like me. I promise her. I will protect her. She has a small son who needs her and is waiting for her. Her husband misses her greatly and all is forgotten of what has happened to me."

With those words, the woman pressed a kiss to her daughter's forehead before gently fading away from my vision.

I opened my eyes and noticed a small red wildflower at the foot of this woman. I bent over and picked it up, before kneeling in front of the woman. I asked her to open her eyes, and then, peering deeply into her soul, I placed the flower in her hands as I told her of the vision I had received. When I finished, she burst into tears.

Then, she started to share her story. She told me how her mother had become consumed by darkness, how demons had taken over her mind. She described how her mother had gone missing and her body was later found by the river — she had taken her own life. The woman before me was convinced that the darkness that had taken over her mother's mind had found a place in her own. She was afraid she would hurt her son or herself, and so she had expelled herself to this wretched Valley for his safety.

I embraced the woman and promised her she would not meet that fate. I prayed for her protection and safe return, and she returned the blessing by kissing my hands.

"Thank you," she whispered. "You are an angel who walks this earth and I will forever be humbled by your generosity and healing."

Already, her eyes were brighter and her energy felt lighter, expanded. I could sense the gravitas in the shadow of this burden she had been carrying, as well as the relief she felt at it being taken from her. Radiating pure love and joy she turned around and started to walk her way out of the Valley.

Yeshua looked at me and smiled. "We can go home now," he said.

As we started to make our way out of the Valley of Death and towards Yeshua's home, he talked to me about fear, as if he had witnessed all that I had seen in my vision with the woman.

"Our greatest challenge in this life is not to feed our fears," he explained. "Fear will take hold of us. It will replay the past over and over again. The more we fear the past, the more we manifest its darkness in our lives. Once we can heal that fear and liberate ourselves from past events, we can also heal our futures.

"To do this we must have faith in the mystery of one's life and blessings from our Father. He will take care of us when we resign our fears and give to Him the burden of which we carry. If we harbour and hold tightly to these burdens, He cannot help us and therefore we cannot be healed of the past. To truly be set free, we must heal the past and be willing to embrace a different reality that is unbeknownst to us."

We walked the rest of the way home in silence as I considered all that I had witnessed and learnt. I was ready to embrace the mystery that was unfolding in front of me. I felt so blessed and humbled to have met this great man who would guide me through the next chapters of my life.

CHAPTER FOUR

Sealed With a Kiss

31: The realized human is fertilized by a kiss, and is born through a kiss. This is why we kiss each other, giving birth to each other through the love that is in us.[3]

— GOSPEL OF PHILIP

AFTER THE EXTRAORDINARY EVENTS that had transpired in the Valley of Death, I decided to leave my aunties so I could dedicate my time to being an Apostle of Yeshua.

Though the other men around Yeshua were not fond of the idea of having a woman amongst them, as it was uncustomary for a woman to study and preach with men, Philip vowed to be my protector. With this promise from my brother, I knew I could rightfully rest in their company. Surprisingly, Yeshua did not contribute

---

[3] The Gospel of Philip, Page 60, Plate 106, Translated by Jean-Yves Leloup, Inner Traditions 2004, p.63.

to the debate over whether I could stay amongst the men. In fact, he did not distinguish between man or woman; his only interest was in my hunger to learn and evolve.

Yet neither Yeshua's acceptance of me, nor Philip's, could bring the matter of my presence fully to rest. During this time, a man called Peter joined our camp, and was not happy to keep my company. One day, as I returned from my morning walk, I overheard Peter threatening to go to the authorities.

"How can we turn our heads in silence? I will go to the rabbis and priests and tell them of this prostitute who is resting with the Son of God."

His flippant comment angered Yeshua, who faced Peter with a wrath that could freeze the rain as it fell.

"You come into my home harvesting lies and hatred," thundered Yeshua. "It is you who calls me the Son of God, yet you are deafened when I tell you that I am the Son of Man."

Peter stood speechless as Yeshua continued. "Perhaps you can learn from this woman, whose name has been tainted for trying to save the sacred life of an innocent child. Learn from her and then you can become my disciple."

At that, Yeshua then left the room. He did not speak a word to Peter for the following forty days.

From then on it was clear that Peter resented me for Yeshua's outburst, and, although we both dedicated our time to spreading his word, we were quite content to coexist in silence.

In the weeks that followed, our group grew larger and stronger. Our home came to include the company of Philip, Andrew, James, John, Peter, Bartholomew, Matthew, Thomas, Thaddeus, Simon and Judas. Martha, Rachel, Sara and Ruth also lived with us, though they spent most of their time preparing the meals and keeping house. The men often ordered me to join the other women, but Yeshua insisted that my role was a special one and I was to hear every single word he had to say to the men.

Every morning I would rise much earlier than the others, out of habit and also because it was my favourite time of the day. Looking back, it was those mornings that I savoured the most. And, if given the opportunity, there is one specific morning I would choose to relive again and again.

Yeshua often joined me on my morning walks, and we would stroll through town, taking in the gentle hum of the wind as it brushed the trees and the peacefulness of the streets that can only come when households are asleep. We would walk, without speaking, until the first bird started to sing. Even then, there was never a need for words between us.

Often, Yeshua would hold my hand and in those moments, just being in his presence, I felt that all truths were known and all fears made nonexistent. He embodied an energy that was pure love, and I would find myself brought to tears just from his nearness.

On that particular morning I wish I could relive again and again, Yeshua woke me much earlier than usual and beckoned me to follow him. It was dark and cold, but he wrapped me in a warm blanket and ushered me outside, where a donkey awaited us. Yeshua helped me get seated on the donkey, then climbed on behind me, gently wrapping his arms around my waist. I felt at home in his embrace and savoured the feeling as we rode quietly through the sleepy streets of Jerusalem.

As the sun started to rise above the distant hills, the donkey led us through the desert towards the East, where the sparkling waters of the Dead Sea were made clear to us.

As we approached the small town of Avnat and made our way to the sea's shore, I was overcome with a rush of emotions and I could not help but cry. Yeshua turned to me and, gently stroking my hair, asked, "Why are you crying, my child?"

I looked at him, but remained silent as I could not explain what was happening to me in that moment. I felt overwhelmed with emotions and feelings. Having experienced this wondrous morning with Yeshua and seeing the sunrise kiss the waters of this incredible inland sea had stirred an avalanche of emotions in me that I could no longer contain. It had awoken a truth inside of me, and I felt like my heart was going to explode.

"What is it?" he asked softly as he looked into my eyes.

I was silent. I didn't have the courage to express to him what I was feeling. I loved him. I was utterly and deeply in love with him. But the thought of saying that out loud terrified me.

Putting a hand on my arm, Yeshua said, patiently, "Mariamne, we can stay here all day in this very spot, and I won't move until you tell me what it is that you want to tell me. What is it you are feeling? I will wait. I am here for you."

We looked at each other as I struggled within myself. I tried to mutter the words, but none came out. How was it that expressing my love for Yeshua would turn out to be one of the most difficult things I'd had to do?

Yeshua sat patiently waiting for me to talk. Gradually, I built up the courage to open my heart to him.

"Because I... I love you," I muttered.

"And what is it about this love that makes you cry?" he asked.

"Because when I am with you, I am free," I told him.

"Then you must ask yourself what freedom you seek," advised Yeshua.

Of this, I was already certain. "The freedom to be with you," I replied definitively.

And as simply and naturally as those words parted my lips, Yeshua leaned towards me and kissed me.

It was the first time that we had kissed, and although the love we shared for each other had been ever present since the day we met, it was in this moment that our love was sealed. I knew we would never turn back.

Yeshua dismounted the donkey and helped me down after him. We walked hand in hand to the edge of the water, watching as a small fishing boat rocked gently near the shore, the water caressing its underside.

Yeshua turned to me and said, "Wait here." Taking off his sandals, he freed his feet and started to walk barefoot through the sand. He then walked through the shallows of the water and, without sinking into the waters, walked all the way to the boat.

Was I seeing things correctly? Did Yeshua simply walk atop the water to the boat? Could it be possible?

As Yeshua took a seat in the boat, he looked at me and started laughing. It was surely my shocked face he was taking such delight in, as I was confused and did not know what was happening. Yet Yeshua continued to laugh and smile at me, as if he was enjoying my perplexity.

"Yes, my dear, I just walked across the plain of water and into this boat for you. What you saw was real," yelled Yeshua across the water.

He always seemed able to read my thoughts.

"And now it's your turn," he challenged with a laugh.

"You want me to walk on water?" I proclaimed.

"Yes! It is in our innate nature to do so. However, many have abandoned their true natures, which limits their abilities. We have forgotten. Though, even you yourself have told me that we are beings of light and therefore we can all walk on water," Yeshua pointed out.

Was I going mad? Was this a dream? Could this really be happening? I asked myself. Yet Yeshua did not budge; he continued to laugh as he watched me vacillate, not knowing what to do.

"Remove your sandals and walk to me," he insisted.

I had no other option than to do what he asked. I leant down, removed my sandals and started to walk barefoot, first through the sand and then slowly through the soft shallow waters.

As I continued to walk, the waters rose higher and higher, reaching my knees and then my thighs.

"Stop! You're not doing it right. Go back and walk to me without sinking," he beckoned.

At his insistence, I returned to the sea's shore and started to once again walk through the shallows. Again, though, I walked through the water.

What Yeshua was asking of me was impossible and I felt ridiculous for even trying. Yet each time I failed Yeshua would insist I go back to the start and try again; and each time the water would rise up to my thighs.

"I can't do this, you've gone mad," I shouted at him across the waters. I was soaking wet and I could no longer hold back my tears of frustration and humiliation. I was defeated, and I stood still stubbornly, refusing to try again. He just smiled and let me stay there for a while. Then, after a few moments, he rose to his feet and yelled across the waters, "Mariamne, I love you!"

At those three words our eyes locked, and it felt as though one thousand butterflies flew up from the pit of my stomach into my chest and throat. He knelt down and touched the water. "Come to me now, I am waiting for you," he said.

With that soft touch that emanated from our love, the waters froze still and became solid, allowing me to walk to him. Crying and soaking wet, I surrendered and embraced the love we shared. My mind was empty, free, as I walked without hesitation towards him. I was walking on water, yet it did not surprise me. With our love we could perform any miracle; our love could move mountains, part the seas or even turn them to land.

When I approached the boat, he stretched out his hand and helped me aboard. As I stepped foot into the boat, the waters instantly turned back to soft, lulling waves.

"Well done, Mariamne," he said, not taking his eyes off me as he pulled me towards him and kissed me once again.

"I think I will take everyone to the Sea of Galilee and teach them this. What do you think?" Yeshua asked me cheekily.

I simply smiled at him and gave him a look that suggested he had truly gone mad. Alas, I knew he was Yeshua and would have it his way no matter what I was thinking.

We sat in each other's embrace for the rest of the morning, laughing like young children. We fished and we sang. We talked about things that were of no importance and, for those few fleeting hours, we pretended to be normal — to know nothing of the greatest of mysteries that had been revealed to us.

It was after this unforgettable day that we started to spend more time together. We shared a special bond and connection that the others could not understand, nor appreciate, but this did not perturb us. We chose to honour our love and be gentle with each other as we allowed it to grow.

When I reflect on these precious times, I think that perhaps it was only Mary, Yeshua's mother who understood what was happening between the two of us. I felt, in a way, that she was glad to see that Yeshua could be so happy and childlike in my company. His days were often filled with long journeys taken on foot, with talking to large crowds and being taken to the homes of the sick. The families of those whom he healed or helped would often house him and insist on sharing a meal with him, and so, we would sometimes go for days without seeing him. Then, as our skills as Apostles grew stronger, it also became our duty to travel and heal the sick, which took each of us away from our home for long periods of time.

On numerous occasions, though, Mary would create an excuse for Yeshua to return to their home, often to tend to his father. I'm not sure how she managed it, but she'd always send me along with him, and the others never said a word.

It was seven miles on foot to visit Joseph, and during the time it took to walk there, Yeshua would tell me things that I was not to share with the others.

He would talk of the lessons that we can only inherit when we die; not a physical death but a spiritual death. He explained how we must first die to ourselves before we can start living. He described how we can die over and over again so that we can live a fuller and greater life.

Often an overwhelming sense of heaviness would come over him. It was as if he could see into the future, as though he knew what was going to happen. He carried this burden with him every day, and I could sense how heavily it weighed upon him. He would stop walking, go silent for a while, say a prayer and look directly into my eyes, telling me:

"Mariamne, remember this, for there will be a time that it will be your duty to share this. Those who will say that I first died and then was resurrected are wrong. For I am already resurrected and will later die. If someone has not been resurrected, they can only die. If they have already been resurrected, they are alive, as God is Alive."[4]

---

4 The Gospel of Philip, Page 75, Plate 121, Translated by Jean-Yves Leloup, Inner Traditions 2004, p.121.

It made me uncomfortable to talk about Yeshua dying, and I found the concept he was explaining to be difficult to understand, but I trusted that there would be a time that I would truly grasp its meaning, and be able to live up to what Yeshua predicted for me.

Until then, I cherished every moment I had with him and thrived in his company.

CHAPTER FIVE

A Secret Ceremony

74: It is through the Breath that we come into being, but we are reborn by the Christ two by two. In his Breath, we experience a new embrace; we are no longer in duality, but in unity.

75: None can see themselves in water or in a mirror unless there is light; none can see themselves in light unless there is a mirror or water to reflect them. This is why we must be immersed [baptized] in water and light; the light is in the oil of anointment.[5]

What is the bridal chamber, if not the place of trust and consciousness in the embrace? It is an icon of Union, beyond all forms of possession; here is where the veil is torn from top to bottom; here is where some arise and awaken.[6]

---

[5] The Gospel of Philip, Page 71, Plate 117, Translated by Jean-Yves Leloup, Inner Traditions 2004, p.105.

[6] The Gospel of Philip, Page 71, Plate 117, Translated by Jean-Yves Leloup, Inner Traditions 2004, p.109.

104: A certain harmony is possible in this world, where man
and woman, strength and weakness, unite with each other...

105: Those who recognize each other know the joy of living
together in this fullness.[7]

— GOSPEL OF PHILIP

YESHUA AND I DECIDED to honour our commitment and
our love to each other, which meant no longer hiding our
affections. Our wedding was to be a small celebration,
mostly kept amongst our family and friends as secrecy
was important due to the popularity of Yeshua's movement and the threat he posed to officials. While it was
hard to believe that Yeshua could be considered a threat
to anyone, the Roman authorities and Jewish rabbis had
already started to spread rumours that Yeshua wanted
to become the King of the Jews — an obvious threat to
the Roman control over Jerusalem and a blatant attack
against the Jewish High Priests. Perhaps there was some
truth to the rumours, as the people would have made
Yeshua their king. But it was never *his* desire. Nonethe-
less, our marriage was to remain silent to protect myself
and the lives of our children-to-be.

We chose to hold the ceremony at Bethany, beyond
the Jordan, and under the direction of John, Yeshua's

---

7   The Gospel of Philip, Page 78, Plate 124, Translated by Jean-Yves Leloup,
    Inner Traditions 2004, p.133.

cousin. At sunrise we planned to gather in the fields alongside the riverbed, where John would be waiting to perform a simple yet beautiful ceremony.

The morning of my marriage, before I had even woken to prepare for the magnificent day, I was stirred by the sounds of gaggling women. As I rubbed my eyes and waited for them to gain clear vision, I was thrilled to uncover my three favourite aunties giggling as they threw rose petals and lavender over my bed. It was such a wonderful surprise and their presence filled me with so much joy.

"My beautiful angels, how did you know about today?" I asked, delighted.

"Philip sent for us," replied Rebekah. "We would not have missed this moment for the world."

She then raised her finger to her lips, hushing me as she gestured to the front door. I quickly rose to my feet and ran to the door, where, standing in the crisp cool morning air, were my mamma and papa. I felt like I was frozen in time, as though I were still that six-year-old girl who would run and wake my parents every morning, embracing them and showering them in kisses. I instinctively threw myself upon them both, embracing them as though I would die if I let them go.

Tears streamed down my mother's face. "My beautiful Mariamne, what a lovely woman you have become. I have missed you so dearly but I am so proud of you. My heart sings with joy every day as the sun shines through my window and God sends me His blessings from you, and in return I send them back to you. I know you have been protecting all of us and and..." She stumbled as the tears and rush of emotions started to choke her throat.

"I simply want to say that I love you, and although I have missed you so dearly, I could not want anything more than your happiness and to share this special moment with you."

Then, my father placed his hand on my shoulder, stoically holding back his emotions, though his sentiments were felt with his presence and that simple gesture, and no words were needed.

With that, my aunties overtook the dwelling and I surrendered to their loving and nurturing care. They massaged every inch of my body with precious oils, fragrant with their prayers and blessings for my new marriage. A perfume of divine anointings for fertility, love, passion, kindness, health and prosperity filled the air, soaking into my skin and cradling my soul. The women braided my hair and delicately placed wildflowers they had picked on their journey around my crown. My mother presented me with her beautiful robes from her marriage ceremony with my father, a gift her grandmother had sent from Egypt. I could not have felt more loved and adored in that moment, as the women of my bloodline bestowed their unconditional love and wisdom on me.

That morning was such an enormous gift that these precious women had given me. It filled my soul with such joy. Having received their doting and blessings I felt truly ready to consecrate my entire being to Yeshua.

When all the fussing and playfulness were complete, we embarked arm in arm on our parade towards the riverbank. The town was starting to stir as the sun commenced its morning trajectory, rising brilliantly beyond the hillside. The birds joined in their chorus, one by one declaring the start of a new day.

I arrived at the Jordan with my mother, father and my dearest aunties, Rebekah, Rachel and Elizabeth, by my side. As I approached, I could see Yeshua in all his stillness and light. He was standing on the edge of the riverbank, gazing into the waters, and when he turned to look into my direction, his eyes shone with light, as if the sun was rising from within his very soul. Not taking my eyes off him, I let go of my father and the women who had accompanied me and I began to walk towards him. When I arrived by his side, he took my hand into his and we stood as one. It was there amongst our dearest family members that we declared our love openly and freely before our God.

An old Jewish priest named Caleb, who was friends with Joseph, Yeshua's father, performed the beautiful ceremony. Yeshua and I's eyes remained locked, and once we were declared husband and wife, John, Yeshua's cousin then celebrated our union with a special baptism. He blessed our bodies, our souls, our minds and our union, praying to our God to alleviate us from all sins of the past and purify us with the cleansing waters of the Jordan. Then, we let go, surrendering to gravity and allowing our bodies to be enveloped by the fresh, cool waters of the Jordan. Our love was baptized in the sacred river and we were reborn in union; our bodies bound for life, our hearts until the end of time and our souls for the rest of eternity.

The night of our marriage would be the first and last evening that we would spend together without the company of our brothers and sisters. That evening, the others stayed in Bethany while we returned to Jerusalem to consecrate our marriage.

When we arrived home, where we discovered a beautiful display of white lilies and the scent of musk perfume, Yeshua took my hand and led me into the Bridal Chamber. It was there that he taught me the secrets of the sacred embrace, a ritual he had learnt from the Jewish rabbis and High Priests when he was growing up.

Yeshua walked towards me and softly ran his fingers down my cheek, my neck, along the caresses of my collarbone and downwards, following the curves of by body to my hips. His touch was gentle, and he drew me closer towards him before slowly undressing my robes. We kissed as he proceeded to remove his own robes. Wrapping his arms around my waist, he drew me even closer towards him. I could feel his breath settle and fall on the base of my neck, as our bodies aligned and melted into each other. Embracing each other, we breathed the same breath and kissed, our hearts beating to the same rhythm and a wave of pure love caressing us.

Letting go of any thoughts, fears or desires, our hands, bodies, breath and hearts entwined. We dissolved into each other and became one another. We were no longer man nor woman, but two beings present in love.

We let our minds, our pasts, our thoughts, our beliefs, our desires, our needs and our preoccupations dissipate into nothingness. We were one. We made love and we became that love.

Through this experience I finally understood what it meant to be in the presence of our heavenly Father. In this oneness we shared, I could truly appreciate His power and splendour. And even if it was solely a glimpse of God's true glory, each and every cell of my body remembered His touch, allowing me to continue to walk in harmony to His tune.

The sacred embrace, which Mary and Joseph had performed when she conceived Yeshua, was the true key to unlocking the secret behind the immaculate conception, Yeshua revealed to me. It is a sacred tradition that has been passed down by many generations of Jewish High Priests to its worthy members. Anyone who is conceived through the sacred embrace is made in the image of God and will remain His child for all kingdoms to come. Those children are born to this earth free spirits and live in harmony with God and all His creatures. Made in the image of God, He exists through us and walks in our shoes on this earth, to fulfil His true will.

A distinct sensation stayed with me that evening; it was gentle but grounded and all knowing. It gave me a strong belief that we had performed this sacred ritual and divine conception. I was convinced we would no longer be two souls, but three, entwined together. And I was grateful for this blessing as I closed my eyes and rested my head on Yeshua's chest, listening to the rhythm of his beating heart. Enveloped by his warm embrace and comforting breath, I fell asleep.

The next morning, I awoke filled with so much joy. I was Yeshua's wife and nothing could have made me happier. I drank in as much of him as possible: his smell, his comforting embrace, his physical strength, his gentle nature and his ever-expanding calmness. I watched as he rose in the morning, finding a comfortable spot by the window to sit and breathe in meditation. Sitting opposite him, I joined him as we breathed together and gave thanks for our blessings and the blessings of the day to come.

Soon, our little bubble was broken as our home was once again filled with chatter and movement. And so, I kept the sacred embrace to myself and returned to my duties and obligations to Yeshua and his plans for all of us.

The first few days of our marriage were the happiest of my life. Sadly, I did not know how brief those days would be. Yeshua, on the other hand, felt that the air had already changed in Jerusalem, and knew that his time was coming to a close.

God had a very difficult path for us to follow, and although I wished I could have simply swept Yeshua up and kept him hidden from the world, keeping him all to myself, I knew something greater than us was at work.

From the moment I met Yeshua, he had always made it clear to me that there would come a day when he would have to part from me. I had never wanted to believe it, because something deep within me believed that we would remain together forever, as, though he had only been in my life for a brief period, I could not imagine an existence without him.

We never spoke of the immaculate conception, but sometime later I missed my monthly moon cycle and my beliefs that a precious being was growing inside of me were confirmed. While he was happy at my revelation, Yeshua pleaded with me to keep the knowledge of our child a secret. He had a dreaded sense that my safety and the safety of our baby would be at risk if the public or authorities were to find out. And so, just as no one was to discover that I was Yeshua's wife, no one could know that I was carrying his child.

I trusted Yeshua with all of my heart, body and mind, and thus found peace in this decision. As much as I would have cherished sharing our news with my loved ones, I trusted Yeshua and gave my desires over to God. In complete faith, I dedicated myself to His path and trusted in His protection.

CHAPTER SIX

Prophecy From the Prophet

What you say, you say in a body; you can say nothing outside this body. You must awaken while in this body, for everything exists in it: Resurrect in this life.[8]

— GOSPEL OF PHILIP

AS STORIES OF YESHUA'S HEALINGS and miracles spread to all corners of the region, it became common knowledge that the authorities were not happy. Each of us could sense the darkness that stirred within the Roman soldiers and the uneasiness that was brooding in their camp. The High Priests felt more threatened with each passing day, and were doing all they could to convince King Herod that he should fear Yeshua.

With tensions arising and our own worry that the

---

[8]   The Gospel of Philip, Page 59, Plate 105, Translated by Jean-Yves Leloup, Inner Traditions 2004, p.57.

Romans could come to arrest us at any time, Thomas and Philip were assigned secret scribes. To protect what Yeshua had taught us, the scribes were appointed to write down and record all that we had learnt, lived and witnessed. Each evening in the darkness of the night, the pages would be taken to a hidden cave in the desert, where they would be safely stored and blessed with prayers for protection.

Yeshua's wisdom, teachings and miracles could not go unrecorded, and in honour of all that he had taught us, we knew it was our duty to continue his work and help awaken the many to the glory of the Kingdom of God.

When I reflected upon all that I learnt and lived alongside Yeshua, I must admit that his greatest lessons came from his endless compassion and immense love, which he shared with all that he met. He taught me how to channel God through my body, my mind and heart so that His words could pass through my lips and heal others. He taught me how the Lord's healing love can travel through our hands and can heal the sickest of the sick.

And so, it became my mission to teach every single person who wished to be free from their poverty, their hunger and their misfortune. I taught them that we are all made equal and that it is not the heaviness of our pockets that gives us freedom, but the fullness of our hearts. This was the true message of Yeshua and this was our path; not just for a select handful, but for all those who sought it.

There were many times I would argue with Peter and his brothers about this. They wanted us to keep these secrets to ourselves, to sell our mystical cures and take the power away from the High Priests. But those were not our roles to claim; we could not exploit the power that was given to us by God. We were to remain open and willing so that God's wisdom could pass through us and be disseminated without charge amongst all beings.

This is because when we open our hearts, God is present, but if we close our minds and open our pockets we only give glory to the false riches of this earth. Riches that can be taken from us as quickly as they are given. Freedom is in the not wanting of material wealth. It is in a lack of wanting that we move forward on our individual paths of spiritual growth and enlightenment. It is the sum of our experiences and everyday being that appreciates the investments of our souls.

As our daily lives became more dangerous, Yeshua decided to send his thirteen Apostles on special missions to preach the Kingdom of God and perform miracles for those God brought to us. Each of our missions would last forty days and would act as a test of our skills as Apostles and our faith in the work we were doing. Perhaps they were also a test of how we would survive without Yeshua by our sides. We were separated into groups of three, with the goal being to reach every corner of the desert, all the way through Egypt and beyond the Mediterranean Sea.

I was fortunate to remain by Yeshua's side. He'd been very protective of me of late and seemed to want to teach me all that he knew. Each evening after a day full of blessings, teachings and sermons, we would retreat to the desert. He refused to sleep anywhere but under the stars during this period, with myself, Philip and Thomas by his side. We would often meditate and give blessings for the food that was gifted to us during the day. Other evenings we would gather without food and the men would simply fast. Yeshua always made sure I had something to eat, however, as my pregnancy was progressing and my appetite had finally returned after the first period of illness I experienced.

On the evenings we spent in the desert, Yeshua would walk away on his own and sit silently. I often watched him, as he meditated and prayed, and I sensed that something was weighing heavily upon him. I worried for his wellbeing, as I could see that he was losing weight and aging rapidly.

When he would return to camp and snuggle next to me, I would stroke his hair and gently place my hands on his forehead, hoping to relieve him of his burdens.

"What healing hands you have, my Mariamne," he would say, before falling asleep in my embrace like an infant child.

I often asked him what it was that troubled him, but

he refused to answer, simply telling me that it was between him and God. Despite his insistence, a sick feeling stirred uncomfortably at the pit of my stomach; something was off and I could sense that darkness was fast approaching.

As it happens, it was our last night in the desert before I would witness Yeshua crumble to pieces. We had given God our praises for the day and shared a warm meal around the fire before retreating to take slumber. Yeshua was restless that evening, and although he tried to take rest with me, something was keeping him awake. I pretended to be asleep, so as to not disturb him, when Yeshua rose to his feet, walking a few yards from our camp.

I sat quietly and watched as he found solace below the expansive starry skies. I witnessed Yeshua dropping to the ground, covering his hands over his eyes and sinking his head between his knees. Unable to do nothing any longer, I approached him quietly, gently placing my hands on his shoulders. Beneath them, I could feel his entire body shaking and realized that he was crying uncontrollably.

He turned to me and wrapped his arms around my waist, nestling his head in my lap. I laid my hands on the centre of his back, behind his heart, and was present for him, like a mother consoling her weeping child.

"I'm so afraid, Mariamne," he wept, his head still

burrowed into me. "I have seen what is to come. The visions have been haunting my dreams here in the desert. Each night my dreams become clearer and detailed. I am so afraid that I cannot go through with what is to come. I have prayed and begged to God for an answer, for strength, for clarity. But even He has turned silent. I feel so lost and alone. Why me? Why has He burdened me with this great task?"

I simply held him and listened to him. I knew that no words of mine could offer the peace Yeshua was searching for. I understood then how strong my Yeshua had been these past weeks, and that these night visions had finally broken him. I wished I could take away his pain and reassure him that everything was going to be okay. I silently asked for God to help me find the right words and I opened my heart and ears to Him.

"Yeshua, God chose you because he knows that you, and only you, are capable of walking this path. He does not give us anything that we cannot handle. Perhaps you can no longer hear Him because He is actually closer to you than ever. He has not abandoned you, but sent me to share this burden with you. Do not close yourself off from me. Do not hide your suffering with a false shield of bravery. I am your wife, and this too I will share with you," I told him, holding him tightly.

We sat under the stars and cried together. I did not let go of him as he wept in my arms, as he surrendered to me and embraced his full vulnerability. There was no need for him to say a single word. I was there for him in that moment and held our space so he could fully relieve himself of all he had been holding onto.

After all the tears had passed through his eyes, he fell silent in my arms and, together, we slept.

The next morning Yeshua awoke a new man. He looked lighter and fresher and had an added energy in his aura. What's more, after travelling from town to town, and camping in the desert for forty nights, he was finally ready to return to Jerusalem. His conversations with God in the desert, and the events of the previous night, had shifted something within Yeshua — a deep healing had taken place and he was prepared to return home.

He would arrive in Jerusalem changed. He was a more reflective and quieter version of himself, yet when he did speak, it would be with a burning determination and clarity. The people would gather and the people would listen. His voice would be heard.

CHAPTER SEVEN

The Last Supper

2: Jesus says: "Do not lie. (3) And do not do what you hate.

4: For everything is disclosed in view of <the truth>.

5: For there is nothing hidden that will not become revealed.

6: And there is nothing covered that will remain undisclosed." [9]

— THE GOSPEL OF THOMAS

AFTER OUR RESPECTIVE MISSIONS, the Apostles returned to Jerusalem, and we planned to reunite at a special dinner where we could share stories of our travels. During our return, Jerusalem was aflutter with preparations for the Jewish Passover, which meant Yeshua and his company could walk the streets a little more freely — though never truly unnoticed.

Yeshua had tasked me with baking bread for Passover,

---

9 The Gospel of Thomas, Translated by Stephen J. Patterson and James M. Robinson , Chapter 6, http://gnosis.org/naghamm/gth_pat_rob.htm.

an undertaking I accepted with pride and joy. I found myself grateful for the wheat and clean water, the fire from which to bake the bread, and my two hands, which were able and fit to knead and work the dough.

Peter was gladdened to see me in the kitchen and took a moment to boast to the others that Yeshua had finally come to his senses and made an honest wife of me. Philip entered as he spoke, and immediately pressed Peter up against the wall, livid with anger. "That woman is your saviour's wife, you will give her the respect that she deserves, or you will get out," growled Philip.

Peter laughed it off and I simply ignored their childish behaviour. I could easily forgive Peter for his remarks and my brother for his rage, as the air in our camp had become tense. A direct reaction to Yeshua's frequent speeches about the fulfilling of the prophecies, and his declaration that the time had come for him to depart from us.

Yeshua often spoke in parables, so we were comfortable with waiting for clarity, and many of the Apostles assumed that the fulfilment of the prophecies was a metaphor that would be made clear in time.

However, since returning from the desert, a dark and dreadful feeling had been stirring within me. I tried to ignore it by blaming it on the pregnancy, and I carried on as though nothing were amiss.

That day, trying to block out my thoughts and fears of what was to come, I concentrated on the piles of dough I was making. By being completely present in the moment, all the background noise of the house simply faded away and I could finally hear the music that stirred from within my inner silence. I worked the dough with my hands and gently moved to my own melody, one I would later sing to my little one.

These small moments of internal escape were bliss for me. Those moments were an opportunity for me to see the world around me more clearly. They gave me the insight I needed to give gratitude and praise for the golden light that beams down from the sun and gently kisses our cheeks good morning. Or for the endless display of twinkling stars that danced to the same tune of my dreams. Those moments helped me see that the magic of God's hand was present in everything around us, and that all we have to do is listen to His whisper and witness His glory.

I rolled out each pile of dough into a round, flat base and placed them next to each other for Martha to cook in the fire. As I was close to finishing the bread preparations, I felt two big, warm arms wrap themselves around me from behind, followed by two hands resting gently on my belly. I closed my eyes and nestled into Yeshua's warmth. No words were ever needed between us, and it was as if he were able to hear the tune of my melody and enter that magical space with me.

Turning me around, he kissed me on the lips and asked me to come with him, for he had prepared something special for the two of us. I collected my shawl, put on my sandals and left the house with my husband.

It was dusk and the streets were busy as men made their way to the Temple, their wives and mothers and daughters at home preparing the sacred meals for the Passover. As we walked along the streets, the busy crowds seemed to pass us by, as if we were invisible. How could it be that Yeshua and I could walk hand in hand against the streams of people and go unnoticed? While it was not a strange experience for me alone, to go unnoticed when walking alongside Yeshua was quite remarkable. However, I did not draw attention to it for fear that if I did, I would destroy the beautiful phenomena that had presented itself to us.

Yeshua led me along a narrow cobblestone path, which led us to the top of a small green hill overlooking Jerusalem. The hill had been transformed into a private garden, filled with plants that bore fruit — from olive trees to pomegranate trees, the garden was bursting with life.

Yeshua sat us down and, together, we rested in silence, watching the sun fade away behind the backdrop of the small city at our feet. I could tell that Yeshua had something important to share with me, but I was not sure if I was ready to hear it.

I turned to him, before he could say a word, and placed his hand on my belly.

"You sit here next to me, your child grows inside of

me. These are the only truths that I want to be present to right now," I said.

Sensing my fear of the words that would inevitably part his lips, Yeshua held my hand and looked straight into my eyes.

"My beautiful Mariamne, I will never be far from you. You have to trust in me and believe me when I tell you this. In the coming days, people will start to betray me, fear will overtake their minds and all that we have achieved together is at risk of being lost. My people love me, but this love can be easily bought. I know you are the only one whom I can trust, and I need you to trust me. What will happen over the coming days is God's will and we must accept it. We mustn't fight it. I chose you to be by my side for a reason. To be my wife and the mother of our blessed child because deep within you is a heart that is so pure and filled with love that no one can take away from you. The light that beams from within you is just a reflection of the love that we share, the love that our Father has given each and every one of us, and the love that you must continue to honour and share with all those you encounter. I've seen dying children come back to life in your arms, women who have been outcast given purpose in their seemingly purposeless lives and man's anger dissipate into thin air in your presence. Your bravery has given me the courage to face this ultimate truth and walk my path to the end, because I know our work will continue through you. I know that every day you will tell our unborn child everything that we experienced, witnessed and shared. Don't be sad for me; be happy for the joy you will give to others."

Yeshua then gifted me a hand-crafted jar he had made for my oils and asked me to perform a special ritual on all the disciples when we got back to the house. He requested that I blend a special mixture of herbs and flowers, and then talked me through the cleansing ceremony I would conduct with him later that evening.

As tears poured down my cheeks, Yeshua kissed me one last time. And although the words could not part my lips, I know he felt the love I carried for him. The love that continues to burn within me.

We made our way back to the house, where Martha had prepared a wonderful meal for everyone. Yeshua had requested that we all be present for dinner and that all arguments that existed between us to be left at the door.

As per Yeshua's instructions, I prepared a bowl of water scented with sandalwood and myrrh. I infused the water with a healing prayer, to allow us to let go of what no longer served us from the past and to ask forgiveness for our mistakes and weaknesses. Alongside Yeshua, we washed the feet of our companions. One by one as they arrived at the entrance, each person removed their sandals, entered the sacred space we had created and joined their hands in prayer, before allowing us to bathe their feet. They would then sit in meditation around the table until the ritual was complete for each and every attendee. When we finished with the men, Yeshua and I washed each other's feet.

Having cleansed our feet and minds, we sat around the table for what we thought would be a celebration of the Passover. However, as Yeshua shared the bread, he did not speak of our Jewish ancestors' freedom from exile. Instead, he spoke of God's wisdom, which he explained must be eaten to become a part of us. The bread resembled God's word, which would nourish and nurture our bodies. The wine, His spirit, which would flow through our veins and become a part of every single cell of our bodies.

Yeshua concluded his sermon by asking us all to remember these blessings he had made and to vow to repeat this ritual in remembrance of every meal we had shared together, every lesson we had learnt and every miracle we had witnessed. That night, we enjoyed a meal together that not only celebrated the gifts that Yeshua had shared with us, but also the beauty of bearing witness to the glory of God, who walked amongst us. Yeshua had opened our eyes to the endless possibilities and the healing potential of God's love and showed us the true path to the Kingdom of Heaven.

When he had finished speaking, Yeshua gave a quiet nod to Judas, who rose from his position at the table and, without saying a word, left our home. We finished the meal without him and Yeshua then requested that all the men accompany him to the garden of Gethsemane, where they would spend the night together praying to our heavenly Father.

The men rose to their feet and started gathering items to take with them. A few of them armed themselves with knives to protect the group and keep watch at night, though Yeshua insisted that was not necessary.

The women busied themselves with clearing the table and packing parcels of bread, seeds and wine for the men. I, however, could not find the strength to move, so I sat at the centre of the table amidst all the activity and simply watched the movement blur around me. I watched and waited as, one by one, the men exited our home and waited for Yeshua outside.

When he was ready to leave, Yeshua walked back into the room where I was sitting. As he came to me, there was a pride and courage in his eyes that told me that though I wanted to grasp onto him and convince him not to go, it would be a battle lost. In my hands he placed a small parcel, which he begged me not to open for three days.

"But I will see you before then will I not?" I asked, looking deeply into his eyes.

"It has begun," he replied before kissing me on the lips and leaving to join the others.

It has begun. What had begun and what was expected of me? I sat there at the table unsure what to think, feel or say. The others left me alone as they continued the cleanup and then made their way home or to bed. Still I sat, staring at the single flickering candle in the centre of the table. It was all that was left of the meal we had shared together only moments earlier. I suspect that I sat there for many hours before I finally rose to my feet, blew out the candle and went to bed alone.

CHAPTER EIGHT

Good Friday

72: *"My God, my God, why hast thou forsaken me?" The
Teacher said these words on the cross, for he had gone to the
place of separation, so as to reunite all that had been separated in God. The Teacher rose beyond death. He became
what he was before the separation. His body was whole, He
had a body, but it was the true body; ours is transient, an
image of our true body."* [10]

— GOSPEL OF PHILIP

WHEN THE SUN ROSE the next morning, I felt as though I
hadn't slept at all. The burden of not knowing what was
to come lay heavy on my mind. I did not know if I was
prepared for, or even capable of, living up to everything
that Yeshua expected of me. But I also knew that all I

---

[10] The Gospel of Philip, Page 70, Plate 116, Translated by Jean-Yves Leloup,
Inner Traditions 2004, p.103.

could do was trust in myself and remain present in the face of that which would unfold.

When I entered the kitchen that day, the effects of whatever events had passed the night before were evident in the faces of the men. Their desperate chatter turned to silence when my presence was made known. James quickly ushered me into the next room, speaking softly and calmly as he explained:

"Mariamne, last night the Roman soldiers arrested Yeshua. Judas led them to us. We tried to protect Yeshua, but he demanded that this was what was to be done."

"But why? Why would Judas have done such a thing?" I asked, in shock and unsure how Yeshua's closest friend and loving disciple could have carried out such a betrayal.

"And Philip, where is my brother?" I begged.

"He is at the courts. He slept outside of Yeshua's cell last night with Peter and they won't leave until they return with him," said James.

At that moment Mary walked into the home with Joseph by her side. She too had just learnt the news. She came to me and pulled me into an embrace; I could feel her heart pounding and her body shivering, but she refused to reveal her fear to the men. Taking a deep breath, she composed herself and, with grace and pride, turned around to address the others.

"We must pray to our heavenly Father during this time, for the strength to love our enemy and the faith that Yeshua will return to his rightful place with us," she declared.

Mary then turned to me and whispered, "You must collect your most dear possessions and come with me. Don't leave any trace of who you are behind."

I nodded and silently went to my room, filled a small basket with my journals, oils, a few shawls and the parcel Yeshua had left for me.

When I was done, Mary linked her arm with mine and said, "This path we must walk alone."

Joseph, Mary and I had walked no more than 200 feet from our home when a group of armed Roman soldiers marched swiftly past us on their way to arrest Yeshua's followers. We had narrowly escaped.

I begged them to allow me to return so I could talk to the officials. I wanted to convince them to release Yeshua, but both Mary and Joseph insisted that I was not to leave their company. And so, we carried on to their home to wait restlessly for some news or a sign of what was to come.

At their home, I prayed to our heavenly Father to reveal something to me. I asked Him to show me what I was to do, and to reassure me that all would be well with Yeshua, that he would return home to me. I prayed that I would be able to hold Yeshua in my arms and that he could remain by my side till the birth of our child. I prayed for his presence, and for his safety. I imagined him next to me, holding our baby for the first time. I felt the immense love as he or she wrapped their tiny little fingers around Yeshua's big one and looked deeply into his eyes for comfort and security. He would be a father who would love and protect them unconditionally. I prayed, I wept and I begged as the actuality of not knowing what was to come started to suffocate me.

It was midafternoon when Philip burst through Mary and Joseph's door. Puffing and out of breath, he had undoubtedly run as fast as he could to get to us.

"They're going to crucify him!" he shouted. "We tried everything we could but the guards just threatened to beat and whip us. We must go quickly."

At his words, I entered into a strange realm. It was as if my soul had been drawn out of my body and I witnessed the events to come from a detached point of view, from somewhere outside of me. I saw myself following Philip through the empty streets of Jerusalem to the centre of town. My heart was pounding, and my head was spinning. I did not know how my legs were moving but I was comforted to have Mary and Philip by my side. Their presence gave me the strength to keep going.

The streets were filled with all kinds of people. Some knew our faces and ran to the officials to give us up as followers of Yeshua. Others whose children we had saved turned their heads as if we were ghosts. All the while, the crowd seemed hypnotized by a madness that made them yell repeatedly:

"Crucify him, crucify him!"

Fists waved in the air and we bore witness to the true power of hatred as it poisoned and infected all those who drank from the cup of lies. Though I am truly unaware of how my body moved, we found ourselves at the front of the crowd. It was there that I saw him for the first time.

Having fallen to the ground on his walk to death, Yeshua was resting on his hands and knees, his body weak and bearing the evidence of a severe beating. Whip lashes covered his back and a crown of thorns had been wrapped around his head, piercing his flesh and causing blood to run down his cheeks, giving the impression that he cried tears of blood.

I could hardly bear the pain that it caused me to watch him in this state, though I could neither take my eyes off him. I knew in that moment he needed my strength. As his wife I had promised to love and honour him in all phases of our life together. And I was determined to love and honour him then, during his weakest and darkest hour.

Suddenly, a stranger burst from the crowd and made his way to Yeshua's side, removing the cross from my husband's back. The guards immediately began prodding him with their swords and yelling at him to put the cross down. He turned to them and said,

"This man saved my son, pray to God that your actions haven't secured your place amidst the fiery flames of hell. For that is what you deserve when you murder the Son of God."

Taken aback by these poignant words, the guards allowed him to carry the cross and help Yeshua to his feet.

It took my husband exactly thirty-three minutes to complete the rest of his journey, and I was by his side for each step, though I did not let him see me until the very end; I knew the pain of seeing me watch him would be almost as agonizing as the wounds that had been inflicted on his body.

Mary and I made our way to the base of the hill, where Yeshua and the two other prisoners who were condemned to death by crucifixion would take their final breath. We held each other tightly and watched as the guards stripped Yeshua of his clothing. Standing naked and fragile like a baby, he looked at us for the first time. Mary's hand was gently resting on my belly, as if trying to spare our unborn child from the pain of losing their father. Yeshua saw this and said:

"Woman, behold your son. Son, behold your mother."

We knew exactly what his words meant. I would behold my unborn child and give praise for every moment I would have with them.

Suddenly, Yeshua was violently pushed to the ground and his body was positioned above the wooden cross, which lay on the ground beneath him. Without a moment to reflect, his torturers drove thick metal nails through Yeshua's hands and feet, pinning his body to the timber as if he were an inanimate ornament. With cold brutality, the soldiers raised, for all to see, the cross that held my husband.

Yeshua now sat high in the air, impaled, bleeding and close to death. His body and last moments were on display for all to witness. I watched helplessly, counting every one of his breaths as I breathed with him. I silently begged him to perform a miracle that would bring him down from that cross alive. I knew he could do it, but I feared he would not. I understood then that these moments were the ominous ending he had been forewarning me of.

Yeshua's breathing started to slow and I could sense his body was close to death. When his breath began to come intermittently, he closed his eyes for the very first time. It was in that moment, as if it were a sign from God Himself, that the clear blue skies suddenly turned ominous. Dark black storm clouds began to roll in from the Dead Sea and fierce winds whistled their way through the now silent streets of Jerusalem. It was as if God was standing there with us, His pain painting the skies black and his tears raining down upon us. Realizing that perhaps they had actually crucified the Son of God, many people went running back to their homes, though others stayed and yelled:

"Bring him down!"

And others: "We must save him!"

For a short moment the rain stopped and a beam of sunlight came streaming through a crack in the dark clouds. The light gently shone on Yeshua's face, giving him the strength and courage to open his eyes and speak one last time.

Looking upwards towards the sky he said:

"Forgive them, Father, for they know not what they have done."

And with those final words he bowed his head and spent his final breath.

Throughout the whole experience, I felt as if every sense of my being was heightened. I could see from different angles, hear people's whispers from far away and even feel the final beat of Yeshua's heart. My heart broke completely in that moment and as the crowd dissipated, I knelt at the base of the cross and wept.

The dark clouds took over and the skies above us erupted in thunder and lightning. The rain poured down on me and I allowed it to wash away my pain as I collected the blood-stained droplets from my saviour into a piece of cloth I'd carried with me.

Hours passed until only a few of us remained by Yeshua's side. When the guards finally brought down his body, I held him for one last moment. Before long, I felt someone kneel down beside me. Surprised, I recognized one of the guards, the husband of a woman I had saved from excess bleeding after childbirth many years ago. He took a firm grip on my elbow and whispered:

"You should leave now or the others will arrest you. I promised your brother that I will return his body to his followers. The guards do not know where it will be taken, and you have my word it will be kept safe."

I looked up into the eyes of this young soldier and could see the guilt and pain he felt for what had just occurred.

"Thank you," I whispered before hesitantly peeling myself away from Yeshua's lifeless body. I gently kissed him on the forehead one last time, rose to my feet and walked away.

That night I had no desire to talk to anyone. I returned to Mary and Joseph's home and cried myself to sleep.

CHAPTER NINE

Herbs and Oils

The Man of Nazareth is the visible of the invisible. 20: Christ contains all: man, angel, mystery, Father.

21: Those who say that the Lord first dies, and then was resurrected, are wrong; for he was first resurrected, and then died. If someone has not first been resurrected, they can only die. If they have already been resurrected, they are alive, as God is Alive.[11]

— GOSPEL OF PHILIP

THE NEXT MORNING I awoke to Yeshua's strong voice; "Mariamne, get up."

As I opened my eyes and rolled over, I truly expected to see him standing near me. Surprised at the emptiness

---

[11] The Gospel of Philip, Page 58, Plate 104, Translated by Jean-Yves Leloup, Inner Traditions 2004, p.53.

beside me, I slowly allowed my eyes to adjust to the sunlight and looked around the room. No one was there, yet I was sure that I had clearly heard a voice. Taking this as a sign not to waste the day, I forced myself to get up. I could hear a murmur of voices outside my room and although I had no desire to see or speak with anyone, I also knew that I was not the only one suffering.

When I emerged, I was pleasantly surprised to see my dear aunties talking with Mary and Joseph. They had taken over the kitchen and were busy making cups of warm brew for everyone. Rebekah noticed me immediately, giving me an enormous smile and an embrace in her cuddly arms. She was my favourite aunt and had taught me everything I knew. She was also the one who had supported me when I'd left to work under Yeshua, making sure that my family didn't cause any trouble in the wake of my decision.

"Mariamne, now is not the time to forget our ancestors or our duties," she said to me as she clung firmly to my arm. "We must prepare the herbs and oils to anoint your husband's body, so that his soul may travel safely to the Kingdom of God. We must ensure that his body remains protected from demons. We must put our own feelings aside and do what we have always done."

I knew she was right, though in all my pain and grief I had forgotten that it was my duty to perform this sacred ritual. It was customary for the widow and the women of the community to gather and prepare the body of the dead with ancient herbs and rituals. The body would then be cleansed with vinegar, anointed with the sacred oils and wrapped in cloth, allowing it to rest peacefully and giving the soul safe passage to exit this plain.

We only had a few hours to prepare everything, and although we could not anoint Yeshua's body that day, as it was the Sabbath, we planned to complete the sacred rite the next morning.

So, in the healing company of my family, I silently asked for strength and guidance from my ancestors above and surrendered to the wisdom of my aunties before we came together to begin the sacred rituals.

We commenced by gathering the women in the master room of the house, where we sat in a circle holding hands. In the centre of the circle I placed the blood-stained cloth that I had been carrying since the day before, which was soaked in the blood of Yeshua. It was the eldest woman's role to lead the ceremony, and when she was ready, she would release a sound that represented the grief and sadness she held within her body.

Margaret was my eldest aunt, and she took lead of the ritual with grace and heart. Once she could feel every woman's energy travelling between our palms, she opened her mouth and let out a long, deep cry. One by one, when we felt the moment was right for us, we joined in. The twelve of us wailed and cried, holding on to each other for support. I could feel a deep, deep sadness welling within me, and when I began to feel that the grief was too much to bear, it was as if the women took it from my body and drew it into their palms. They wailed for Mary, they wailed for my unborn child and they wailed for me. We held onto each other, wailing and crying. Finally, when no more sound could come from our voices, we sat still, sobbing in silence. And when no more tears would come, we held each other's hands, looked deeply into each other's eyes and simply smiled. Our smiles and lightness of being eventually turned to laughter, and we sat and laughed and cried until finally, I felt as though a huge weight had been lifted from my body. I felt light again; ready to continue my journey.

Our circle was complete, which meant that we were ready to prepare the herbs and oils. Each of us took to completing different tasks, some preparing the cloth that would bind the body of Yeshua and others gathering and cleansing the jars to prepare them for the sacred oils. Myself and the three elders set to preparing the herbs, delicately drawing the oils from the flowers and leaves, so as not to destroy them but to enhance their healing powers. Before mixing them with oil we would breathe words of light and wisdom into each one and ask the spirits to help guide and protect the now dearly departed.

Each plant had its own unique energy and healing potential, and my aunties had taught me how to communicate with the essence of each of them, nurturing their potency and extracting their nectar.

By dusk, all the women placed their items into a basket. This indicated that everything was ready for the final phase of our ceremony, which would begin the next day. The men were again allowed back into the home, and everyone was invited to stay for supper.

I, however, chose to retreat early for the evening, going to bed without supper and sleeping a deep, dreamless sleep.

CHAPTER TEN

On the Third Day, the Son, He Rose

1: But they were grieved. They wept greatly, saying, How shall we go to the Gentiles and preach the gospel of the Kingdom of the Son of Man? If they did not spare Him, how will they spare us?

2: Then Mary stood up, greeted them all, and said to her brethren, Do not weep and do not grieve nor be irresolute, for His grace will be entirely with you and will protect you.

3: But rather, let us praise His greatness, for He has prepared us and made us into Men.

4: When Mary said this, she turned their hearts to the Good, and they began to discuss the words of the Savior.

5: Peter said to Mary, Sister we know that the Savior loved you more than the rest of woman.

6: Tell us the words of the Savior which you remember which you know, but we do not, nor have we heard them.

7: Mary answered and said, What is hidden from you I will proclaim to you.

8: And she began to speak to them these words: I, she said, I saw the Lord in a vision and I said to Him, Lord I saw you today in a vision. He answered and said to me,

9: Blessed are you that you did not waver at the sight of Me. For where the mind is there is the treasure.

10: I said to Him, Lord, how does he who sees the vision see it, through the soul or through the spirit?

11: The Savior answered and said, He does not see through the soul nor through the spirit, but the mind that is between the two that is what sees the vision and it is.[12]

— THE GOSPEL ACCORDING TO MARY MAGDALENE

I WOKE THE NEXT MORNING at the crack of dawn, slipping quietly from my bed and preparing myself so I could go to my saviour's resting place. Although it was customary for all the women to complete the final anointing together, I purposely did not disturb the others as I wanted to go alone. This was a decision based on the

---

12 The Gospel According to Mary Magdalene, Chapter 5, http://gnosis.org/library/marygosp.htm.

safety of everyone else — and to avoid drawing attention to the location of Yeshua's body. I knew that James and Philip had worked so hard to prevent the Romans from finding the place he was to be laid and I most certainly did not want to jeopardize that.

I gathered all that we had prepared the previous day and slipped out of the house unnoticed. As I walked the long path to Yeshua's tomb, I pondered how I would continue on in this life without holding Yeshua's hand or feeling his breath warm on my cheek as he slept by my side each night. I felt grateful that I would soon have one last moment to see him and hold him.

As my long walk neared to an end and I got further along the path, I could see the sun as it started to rise behind the hill where Yeshua's tomb lay. A golden light shone down upon it and smothered it with golden rays of sparkling light. The vision instantly filled my heart with hope and a sense that everything would be okay. I knew he was waiting for me and to him I would go.

As I traversed the final stretch and got closer to the tomb, I was surprised that no one stood guard. Philip had told me the men were sharing the responsibility of keeping guard both day and night, but when I looked around for someone, perhaps sleeping under a nearby tree, I found that there was no one in sight. Perplexed, I began to worry that I could not possibly roll the stone that blocked the entrance to Yeshua's tomb.

When I eventually made it to the entrance of the

tomb, my heart started to race at seeing that the stone had already been rolled back. I picked up my pace, running inside the tomb, I was shocked to find nothing. His body was gone. The tomb was empty save for a few remnants of Yeshua's clothing, which lay motionless in the centre of the hollow, cold, dark cave.

It was as if my heart was broken all over again. Dropping to my knees, tears started to run uncontrollably from my eyes. I clenched my hands together, entwining my fingers and squeezing so hard that my knuckles turned white. Then, I began to pray.

"Dear Lord Father,

I know that it is You who requested our beloved Yeshua to rejoin You in Your Kingdom. But I pray that he is by your side and no further harm has come to his body or spirit.

Please give me the strength to continue without him and open my eyes to the path that I am meant to take. I feel so alone and my eyes are now blinded by the darkness of that unknown. My faith is strong, but my heart is bleeding. Give me a sign; something. Show me what is meant for me now, for I am a child without a home, a wife without a husband and mother without a name."

Sitting in the middle of that tomb, I sobbed. My heart was desperate for one last chance to see, to touch, to smell and to hold my Yeshua. As I sat there feeling abandoned and alone, I noticed a shadow travel across the entrance of the tomb. I started to wipe the tears from my eyes, trying to focus on the light at the entrance of the tomb, where it seemed — though my eyes were swollen and my vision blurred — the silhouette of a man stood.

"Who's there?" I cried out. "Where have you taken my husband's body?"

"Hush, my child," said the voice.

I instantly felt at ease at the sound of this voice, it was familiar to me. I stood there and listened.

"Have you already forgotten all that I have taught you? All that was lived and that you will keep living? Don't cry for the dead and don't cry for me. Those who inherit the dead are themselves dead. Those who inherit the Living-One are alive, and they inherit both the living and the dead. The dead do not inherit anything. For how will the dead inherit? When a dead man inherits the Living-One, he shall not die; rather, the dead shall live.[13]

"Tell the others I am not dead but alive. Alive in the hearts of all those who have listened to my words and opened their hearts to the Lord. Rejoice in the life that we shared and let me live through your words, your kindness and your love.

"I love you, Mariamne, and I will always be with you."

With those final words the shadow faded away, leaving behind the sun's morning rays, which pierced

---

[13] Text of the Gospel of Philip, Page 37, Plate 100, Translated by Jean-Yves Leloup, Inner Traditions 2004, p.53

through the entrance of the tomb, shedding light on its darkness and warming its cold, damp interior.

I ran to the entrance of the tomb where the shadow was standing, but no one was in sight.

"I love you too, my dear Yeshua," I whispered to the wind.

CHAPTER ELEVEN

The Reckoning

> *As for Wisdom who is called "the barren," she is the mother*
> *of the angels. And the companion of the [...] Mary Magda-*
> *lene. [...] loved her more than all the disciples and used to*
> *kiss her often on her mouth. The rest of the disciples [...].*
> *They said to him, "Why do you love her more than all of us?"*
> *The Savior answered and said to them, "Why do I not love*
> *you like her? When a blind man and one who sees are both*
> *together in darkness, they are no different from one another.*
> *When the light comes, then he who sees will see the light,*
> *and he who is blind will remain in darkness.*[14]

THE GOSPEL OF THOMAS

BEFORE LEAVING THE TOMB, I gathered the clothing of
Yeshua and placed it in my basket next to the jars of
oils and swaddling. I knew that if I walked into town

---

[14] Perkins, Pheme (2009). Introduction to the Synoptic Gospels.

with these items I was sure to be arrested, so, as I left the tomb, I walked around to the harsh, steep hillside behind the tomb where large rocks clung to the hill's shoulder, seemingly fragile but looming with an ominous danger that would wreak havoc if one was to fall.

Amidst the dry, rocky landscape, a small lemon tree had sprung free from its roots and reached for the sky in full blossom. Who was not to say that God was not everywhere? I thought to myself. Even amidst these rocks, His spirit raised up and presented this miracle of a tree. Seeing it as a sign, I walked carefully up to the tree and placed my belongings under its shade. I knew they would be safe there.

As I started to walk back towards the tomb's entrance, I was stopped in my tracks by the sound of men arguing. I waited, still and silent, and listened to their voices.

"We must leave; we will all be dead by dawn if we don't go. Yeshua has gone. He has abandoned us. Maybe everything was just an illusion, but unlike Yeshua, I will fight for my life. I will not let them take me and kill me like this!"

I knew that voice well. Peter. Confident that the small group of men were my fellow disciples, who would not cause me harm, I came out from behind the tomb and approached them. Looking to my left, I was surprised to see that the rock had been pushed back in front of the tomb's entrance.

Andrew saw me first and hushed the men to quiet

their quarrelling. I could see Peter was not happy to see me, he could not meet my eye, and I suspected he was embarrassed by his words. In the others, I sensed heartbreak and confusion. Their mourning was no less painful than mine, and words of war and fighting would not help them now.

"Stop!" I demanded. "Stop, all of you. Yeshua did not give up and he did not die. He is alive. He came to me in a vision this morning when I came to anoint his body. The stone, which is now covering the entrance, was rolled back and his body was gone. He does not need his body, as he has risen to a new level of existence."

Turning his back on me and facing the men, Peter once again began to talk to the group.

"This woman has gone mad! Do you really think she could have rolled back this stone by herself?" The men started to murmur amongst themselves, while Peter's voice got more powerful and louder.

"Why would our saviour, who chose us men to be his ministry, reveal himself to a woman? Look into her eyes, men; she is, and always will be, a sinner who tried to tempt our Lord into the darkness. Now that he is dead, she rejoices in fables and fantasy."

"But why should we not listen to her?" asked Thomas. "She spent more time with Yeshua than any one of us. Why would he not reveal his risen self to her now? You have always disliked her, but that does not mean she does not speak the truth."

"Then he would have revealed himself to all of us," replied Peter with determination in his eyes.

I could see now that fear had entered these men's hearts, and that Peter's words would eventually win them over. But I could not blame them for this. Though I felt abandoned by the men I had once called my family, with tears in my eyes, I addressed them one last time.

"Open the tomb and see for yourselves. Inside you will not find the body of Yeshua. I pray that you may see the truth of his love and that it will burn brightly within each of you."

With those final words, I turned my back on the men and began my return to town. I had found strength in my own words and trusted the wisdom that now burnt brightly inside of me. Yeshua would live as long as his love and his words lived within me. I was humbled and grateful for all that he had given me, and I made a promise to myself in that moment, that I would always live true to all that had passed. I would bring my husband's profound wisdom into the future with me, with every step I would take, until my very last breath. This was my promise to him.

When I had travelled what must have been a mile down the track, the sounds of vultures screeching captured my attention. It felt as if their calls were echoing in my head, though when I looked around I could not see them. Suddenly, one flew directly over me, barely missing me, before landing around the corner. Walking off track, I followed the twisted landscape towards the sounds of the birds, which led me to a small clearing. As I walked closer, a shiver rushed down my spine and I felt a deep sadness sweep through me. But it was not *my* sadness; the ground, the rocks, the trees carried this sadness. It was dark and dense and heavy. It felt as though it were squeezing down upon my lungs and choking me, though for reasons I cannot name, I felt the urge to keep moving ahead.

My steps were shaky, and I slowed down so as not to tumble. Focusing my attention on the earth beneath my feet, I took two small steps before raising my head again. The sight that awaited me was one I would never wish upon another. A single large dead tree stood tall and barren. From its stretched-out white branch hung a man's lifeless body, vultures eating away at his flesh. It was Judas.

I did not know why I was called to witness that site, but I knew Judas's soul deserved to find peace. He'd been a good man and a good friend at one time. And though I do not know why he had betrayed Yeshua, there was no doubt in my heart that he'd only done what had been asked of him.

The sight of his body was horrendous, and I could not bear to look at it. As I turned away, I noticed a newly sprouted patch of fresh green. I walked over to the small area, knelt down and said a special prayer for Judas.

I prayed his spirit would be free and that he would receive all the forgiveness he was seeking. I gave him my own forgiveness for his actions, and I sent him my love. I prayed that the angels would protect his soul with love and light and join his spirit on its journey as it departed our land and travelled to its final destination in the Kingdom of God. I prayed Yeshua would reunite with him and that Judas would finally find the peace he so deserved.

As my prayers left my heart and travelled up to caress the decaying body of Judas, I saw the vultures begin to fly away, one by one. I kept sending my prayers until the birds were gone, leaving Judas's body to rest. I found peace in the fact that his body was now protected and I knew that his spirit would find a safe path to his final destination. At that knowledge, I felt an overwhelming sense of calm and serenity fill my heart, which allowed me to finally rise to my feet and continue walking the path back home.

CHAPTER TWELVE

The Escape

MARY WAS RELIEVED to see me return to the house. My friends and family were stricken with panic at rumours that the Romans had started arresting anyone who had anything to do with Yeshua. It was being said that King Herod was now worried that in the wake of Yeshua's death his people would cause an uprising. To keep the peace, his soldiers were being sent to arrest anyone known to have kept Yeshua's company.

"Mariamne, listen to me," said Mary. "You have to go. Joseph and I have organized a safe passage for you this evening. You will be taken to Alexandria, where a boat will be waiting to take you to the new land. There you will be kept safe from the Roman Empire, and the Jews will never know you existed."

I was stunned. "But I can't leave. I'm with child, and my child must be born in Jerusalem. You know this — you know I have to stay," I pleaded.

"Mariamne, I know how scared and afraid you are," Mary said gently, "but if you stay, tragedy will fall on you and this baby. Word will get out, they will kill you both. I beg you to go, and I promise that we will send word when it is safe for you to return. God only knows how much I wish to meet my grandchild. He or she is all that I have left of my Yeshua, but I am willing to sacrifice my relationship with that child so that they may live. Yeshua lives on through you. You have to protect all that remains of him, for all of us."

"But what about you and Joseph? What will happen to you if I go?" I asked.

"We will be fine," she assured me. "We will head back to Bethlehem until the time is right for our return. Joseph is aging, so we cannot take the long journey with you, but Philip will accompany you. Go, my child, and prepare your things."

At that, she gave me one of her all-knowing nods, then turned and walked away.

I knew what Mary said to be true. I could not risk the life of my child. Although my heart was in Jerusalem, I had to go. I spent the next few hours writing letters to my loved ones and packing the few possessions I had left. I wrote to my family in Magdala and told them of the glorious man that was Yeshua and I thanked them for sending Philip to Jerusalem. As destiny would have it, he would save my life not only that day in the market, when he sent Yeshua to me, but also this day, as we began our journey into the new world.

We ate in silence that evening, no one wanting to share a word of what would become of our futures. It went without saying that we were humbled to have shared this important part of our lives and grateful for what would be our last meal together.

When supper was finished, Joseph handed me a small sack of gold coins. "The angels will protect my fair girl," he said. "This is for you and your child. It is not much but it is enough to keep you safe and get you to your destination. When you are there, bless the ground as you take your first steps and it will forever be your protector."

How like Joseph this was; he had always been a man of few words, one who when he did speak always spoke with dignity and profound wisdom.

"Thank you, Joseph," I replied as I embraced him. For the first time, I did not want to let go. Not only did I feel safe in his arms, but I knew that when I finally let go, my time in Jerusalem would be over. And yet, I peeled myself from his embrace and set forth on my journey away from that magnificent city — the city which had taught me so much. It had been the home of such wondrous insights, discoveries and love, but would also forever bear the scar of deep heartaches and injustices. Injustices I could not risk exposing my precious child to.

Drawing together all of my courage, I placed my trust

in that tiny spark of light that forever resided deep within me. I was determined that from that point on I would allow it to guide me and shine a light upon the path that would become my future. I was confident that with every uncertain step towards what lay ahead, mysteries would always be unveiled to me.

Without looking back, I walked out of that small, humble stone cottage, which had always been a place of shelter, sustenance and protection for me, and walked straight into the arms of my brother, who stood strong in the darkness of our departure. He took my hand and swiftly guided me onto a donkey so we could begin our journey out of Jerusalem. As we approached the city gates, we received what could only be viewed as a sign from the angels that we had their protection — there lay two Roman guards, passed out, surrounded by empty jars of wine and the telltale signs that they'd recently kept company with local prostitutes. Their debaucherous activities allowed us to leave Jerusalem without being noticed.

We travelled through those gates with pride and strength, ready to officially begin our long journey into the desert. When tiredness got the better of us, we found a safe spot to rest for the night. Philip laid the ground with carpets and, tired and drained of all words, thoughts and emotions, I lay next to him, resting my head on his shoulder. As I snuggled into his warm and strong embrace, I listened to his soft voice as he began to confess to me what had happened in the garden of Gethsemane when the Roman soldiers had come to arrest Yeshua.

"Prior to the Roman soldiers' arrival, Yeshua had asked us to pray for him," Philip explained. "He was afraid and he asked us to stay awake with him and pray, but we were very tired, and we betrayed him, abandoning him in his true time of need by falling asleep. I feel so ashamed.

"We later awoke to the sounds of the Roman soldiers coming up the path. Judas was with them, he had led them to Yeshua. He walked straight up to Yeshua and kissed him on the cheek. It must have been a signal to the Romans who Yeshua was; I cannot explain it any other way. I do not know what had happened to Judas, for he was such a devout follower. It still doesn't make any sense. The guards then approached Yeshua. Simon and Peter were both armed with knives and tried to defend him — Simon cut off the ear of one man — but Yeshua simply walked to the injured soldier, healed his ear, and then turning his back on all of us and walked away with the soldiers. He didn't say a word. Mariamne, I betrayed him. I will never forgive myself."

"Hush, my brother," I soothed. "It is too late now to regret what has happened. I believe deep in my heart Yeshua knew what was planned and even welcomed it. One day, we too might find the strength to do the same."

We left it at that and the both of us sat in silence,

trying not to think about the last few days, until we succumbed to tiredness and fell asleep, there in the desert
beneath the stars.

The next morning, we awoke as the sun began to rise
above the distant sand dunes. I noticed that Philip was
looking at me strangely, seemingly concentrating on
my face and features. "What are you doing?" I asked,
slightly deterred by his stare.

"We have to make you look like a man," he said.

"What?" I asked, shocked.

"I had a dream telling me that the only way we could
enter Alexandria was if you were dressed as a sick man.
As though we were arriving in Alexandria seeking a cure."

Philip then spat into his hands, collected some dust
from the ground and began to rub it into my face. He
took a few pieces of clothing from his belongings and
dressed me in them. He had me promise not to speak a
word. And then, we continued on our three-day journey
into Alexandria.

It was as we trekked through the desert that I remembered the gift Yeshua had handed me the day before he
was executed. In secret, when Philip and I were resting,
I took out the delicate parcel. It was small and wrapped
in plain cloth. When I opened it, I discovered it contained a chain with a pendant. The pendant was made
of silver and featured a beautiful hand-crafted rose in
the middle of a cross. A letter accompanied the gift.

My dearest Mariamne,

I can only imagine that the past days have been tough for you; no doubt you are beginning to question it all. I give you this gift as a reminder of your true path. A path that began long before you met me. It grew in the shadows of our love, and you must continue to honour it without me.

May this gift not be a symbol of our greatest fears but a reminder of our faith and all that we have suffered to open the hearts and minds of God's children. My sacrifice is for their greater good and the greater good of all mankind. Do not mourn for my loss, but celebrate all that you have learnt and gained. May the love in your heart give you a rich life and guide you during the darkest of hours. Let your love give light to your path and keep you safe so you can tell our story, for you have borne witness to it all.

Do everything you can to teach and protect the very precious child you carry. Our two souls invited him into this world and he or she will do great things, as I am certain that you shall also achieve great things. Please do not be fooled by the illusion of separation for I am always by your side. I am you and we will always be as one.

Yours,
Yeshua

I held the precious letter in my hand and savoured every word. I put on the necklace, the pendant resting close to my heart. It was a true reflection of how close Yeshua would always be to my heart. I vowed then that I would honour his words and keep him alive within me.

CHAPTER THIRTEEN

Arrival in Alexandria

WHEN WE FINALLY ARRIVED in Alexandria, the city was buzzing with activity. Market men tended their stands; women walked freely with their children; philosophers took stage on every corner, gathering crowds as they discussed the influence of the moon and the stars.

A soft breeze swept in from the nearby port, bringing with it air that was sweet and salty. I could feel a sense of freedom in Alexandria. It was as though no one was afraid of one another, as though there was harmony between different theologies, races and classes. The craftsmen worked with smiles on their faces, students strolled with a spring in their step, and women walked with confidence, their hair flowing long and bold behind them.

My attention was quickly taken by a beautiful young woman wearing white robes, with gold leaves embroidered around the shoulders and neckline of her trappings. I watched her as she playfully threw grapes into the mouth of a young admirer, before cheekily slapping him across the back and running away, telling him he knew nothing of destiny. I was surprised to see that no one looked on with judgement; in fact, no one seemed to pay any particular attention to her at all. Watching her made me suddenly aware of myself, of my oversized men's robes and the horrid dirt on my face. I longed to be that girl — to feel her sense of freedom, uninhibited joy and playfulness.

We'd only just arrived and this colourful city was inspiring me with a dream to unveil my hair and talk to the crowds as a free woman. But just as my imagination started to run wild with hopes of free expression, Philip tugged me close to him and reminded me not to say a word. It was as if Philip could read my mind, and his stern look reminded me that we would not be safe until we had crossed the Mediterranean Sea.

Philip guided me to a small open square with a fountain in the centre, telling me to wait there as he tied his belongings to the donkey and headed up a small, cobblestone street. I rested gently against the donkey and watched the water bubble freely from the spurt of the fountain. I closed my eyes and listened to the sounds of the water and the humming of the city. Heavy footsteps, laughing children, chirping birds, quarrelling neighbours, the whistle of the wind as it blew in from the desert. As I stood there waiting for Philip, I melted into these sounds.

My quiet moment, however, was soon interrupted by a slight tug on my dress. I opened my eyes to see a small boy of about five years old standing beside me. Looking up to me with big blue eyes, he asked, "Sir, can you help me drink the water?"

Taking his hand, I walked him over to the fountain and cupped the fresh, cool water in my hands. His tiny hand clutched my arm as he leant over and slurped the water. His gentleness and trust in me reminded me of Yeshua. We are all born with such purity, trust and innocence — why must we lose this when we grow older? I asked myself. If we were all children of God, why did age slowly pollute man's heart with darkness?

Without acknowledgement or a word of thanks, the young boy ran back into the city streets.

"You can heal the water but can the water heal you?" I heard ripple through the now-empty square.

"Excuse me," I replied, turning in the direction of the voice. In the distance I discovered a slight, skinny woman with wild, curly gray hair. Her eyes were black and intense as she continued to babble and walk towards me.

"You carry a secret that will cause men to shed their blood, women to burn and children to be drowned. You think you carry light, but it will only bring darkness. Turn to the West and glorify it, for the sun and moon do not want you. Cling to the ground and weep for mercy, for no one will let you walk free. You hold a secret that will destroy us all."

When the woman had finished her rant, she began to mutter gibberish to herself, then headed away from me to the other side of the square. My heart beat quickly, but I could not find words to give back to this woman who had insulted me with her prophecy. Instead, I watched as she disappeared into the buildings and uttered a small prayer to God to protect me from evil spirits and the work of the devil. I knew her words could only have come from the devil himself, and I would not let his work persuade me. I took a deep breath, trying to compose myself, before noticing a young nobleman standing across the square, watching me curiously.

"Why did you not speak back to that woman? Are her words true?" he asked me.

Remembering that I was dressed as a man, I made a small grunt that I hoped suggested I didn't think anything of it, but still the man would not take his eyes from me.

"Where do you come from? Your robes are nothing I have seen from here and your donkey is without a braid or a bell."

I looked down and hunched over, hoping that, with my silence, the man would lose interest in me.

"I saw you with the boy before. You are different than

those of us who are from here. Who sent you and what are you looking for?"

I knew that his insistence meant he would not give up easily. So, in a low crackling voice, I whispered:

"I'm nothing but a poor, sick man seeking a cure. I come from Galilee."

"Well, I am a student of the court and I have medicine to cure any illness," said the man as he walked to me, staring directly into my eyes. "But something tells me you are not who you say you are."

In that moment, the young man raised his arm and swiftly whipped the veil from my head. He then proceeded to tear open my robes at the chest, revealing my feminine curves.

"And indeed you are not!" His breath now hovering over my ear as he pressed his hand into my breast.

"Get your hands off me, I am a married woman," I pleaded.

"Oh, you don't look like that to me," the man replied, clearly unaware of my rounded belly, as he moved his body closer to mine, rubbing his now grossly swollen member against my leg.

"I can, and will, do what I want with you."

His hand gripped my face as he tore the top of my robes open even further, revealing my bare breasts to the square. His other hand travelled across my hips and slid its way between my legs.

"Please don't!" I begged him.

But my pleas only seemed to excite him more. Pulling my head backwards, the man pushed me against the wall and forced himself onto me.

"Stop," I pleaded, tears running down my cheek. "I am with child!" I attempted. And with those four simple words the young man stopped, pulled himself back and looked down at my round, swollen body. Placing his two hands on my belly, his eyes welled with tears.

"Oh, God, what have I done?" he said, now visibly shaken. "I don't know what came over me. Please forgive me," he continued, slowly bringing my robes back to my chest and shoulders.

With his head hanging low, he left the square as I crumbled to the ground, shaking and crying. Why was this all happening to me? I wondered. How I wished I could go back in time and lie safely in the arms of Yeshua. How I wished to feel his warm embrace around me and to listen to his sweet voice. I stayed there, crying, and prayed that Philip would return quickly. But the sun would soon be setting and I had no idea what we were meant to do next, of what the plan for our escape would be.

Hours passed by, but still there was no sign of Philip. When I could wait no longer, I placed my trust in my inner guide and untied the donkey. I walked slowly down the path where I had seen Philip go earlier that day. The street was quiet, doors were closed and families remained inside together. When I reached the end of the road, I saw that it opened up into a large square that sat at the base of an enormous Temple, which seemed to be connected to a noble palace. Curious about the building, I approached its entrance, not letting the two soldiers who kept guard deter me.

The inscription on the entrance of the Temple above the gates read:

Quod est inferius est sicut quod est superius, et quod est superius est sicut quod est inferius, ad perpetranda miracula rei unius

That which is below is like that which is above, and that which is above is like that which is below. All miracles are of only one thing.

Something about the inscription made me feel safe, and as I took refuge in a small archway on the other side of the square, I pondered its message. Soon, night fell with still no sign of Philip. My eyes became heavy, my head fell forward and when I could no longer hold myself awake, I succumbed to the gentle rocking of my breath and the double heart beats that pulsed inside of me, falling into a deep sleep.

CHAPTER FOURTEEN

The Great Library

WHEN I WOKE the next morning, I was surprised to find myself lying on the floor of an unknown space. At first, panic struck me, and I quickly took to my feet. I saw that the room I was in was large and filled with works of art and drawings. The blanket that had kept me warm was made from animal fur, making it clear that I was not in the household of your average citizen.

From somewhere outside the room, I could hear the soft sound of a woman singing. I followed its soft, sweet vibration until I could hear it echo off the walls and bounce all around me. Her voice sounded like an angel, so pure and full of light, and it drew me in its direction until my eyes finally fell upon the woman I felt was calling to me.

In the centre of a large, circular room knelt a slender female dressed in white. Green leaves filled her hair and she sat with a single lit candle clasped in her hands.

With her eyes closed she continued to sing, and it was as if her voice danced around the angle-less room and swirled upwards into the ceiling. Looking up through the open-air circle of the rounded roof above me, I could see the first sparkles of sunlight twinkle their way down to earth.

Perhaps unaware of my presence, the woman continued to sing, and her tune drew me closer towards her. Though I did not know the words, my mouth opened and I started to hum along to her song, feeling as though a choir of angels came fluttering from my voice. The woman at the centre of the room opened her eyes and turned towards me. Our eyes locked and we continued this song of prayer together.

Once the hum found its way around the room and up and out the centre of the roof, we stopped and stood in silence before one another. She blew out the candle, then began to move towards me.

"My name is Ophelia. Welcome to my home," she said.

"You have the most beautiful voice," I told her. "May I ask who you were singing to?"

"I was singing to the centre of the universe. I sing for peace upon our land, prosperity for our crops and the wisdom to understand the greater truth of man."

Taking my hand, she ushered me to follow her. She walked me through an immense palace and into what I could only assume were her chambers, where she asked a servant to bring some warm water. She began to stroke my frizzy, wild locks, running her fingers through my hair and down around my shoulders. She smiled softly at me and began to undress me.

"Let me bathe you," she said.

As she removed my old dirty robes, she discovered my enlarged belly, which seemed to grow bigger each day. Still smiling, she took my hand and led me to a bath. The room was filled with marble and servants stood in each of its four corners. She guided me into the steaming waters, and with her bare hands she slowly washed my skin with water perfumed with lavender and musk.

Ophelia was gracious and kind, and while she bathed me, she spoke to me about her people, the sacred Temple that adjoined the palace we were in and the great library.

I told her little except that I desperately needed to find my brother, and she swiftly sent a few of her servants to investigate, promising me that I needn't worry because all things were in their correct order.

Later that morning, Ophelia showed me around the palace and introduced me to the community she called her family. Her home was filled with servants, who were also students of the universe and offered their services in exchange for ancient knowledge and wisdom. Ophelia lived with twelve elders, who acted as head council for the city and liaised with the Roman Empire. She had five younger sisters and an older brother who was preparing to become a soldier of the light, though when I asked what that meant she said it was much too complicated to explain.

She spoke softly but always with an air of confidence and deep knowing. She was unlike any woman I had ever met and I was immediately inspired to be more like her.

"Can you tell me what the inscription means on the front of the Temple?" I asked. The words had left my lips before the thought could even enter my mind. I had meditated on that inscription last night before finding myself inside the palace and I was certain she knew of magic and all things that were forbidden in Jerusalem.

Bringing her index finger to her lips to keep me quiet, she took my hand and walked me towards a small corridor, where huge tapestries hung from arched walls. She ushered me to follow her towards a large marble statue placed in front of a solid brick wall. Sliding herself behind the statue, Ophelia placed her two hands against the wall and pushed it open, seemingly without effort. Smiling, she motioned for me to join her.

After we squeezed through the small entrance, she closed the door behind us, and I took in the cold, damp space, which smelled like wet marble on a winter's day. It took a while for my eyes to adjust to the darkness but the passage slowly came into sight, and I saw that we were standing in a small, carved-out tunnel. A series of lanterns flicked specks of light that led the way down a long dark walkway.

We walked for an age before the passage opened slightly to reveal a large wooden door. Ophelia reached her hand beneath her robes and pulled out a large bronze key. She clicked the key into the door's lock, twisted it and slowly pushed it open, motioning for me to enter before her. Taking two steps forward, I found myself in the centre of a huge room with scrolls and manuscripts stacked from the floor to the ceiling.

"To understand the true meaning of that inscription, one must first read all of these," said Ophelia.

"But something tells me you have knowledge that also belongs in our library," she continued. "When the time is right, you will leave it behind and I will keep it safe for you."

I was in absolute awe of what stood before me. It appeared that I was looking at hundreds and hundreds of years of writings, teachings, rituals and more.

"Have you read them all?" I asked.

"No," she replied with a slight smirk. "But I do know most of it. Come, let me show you something."

Taking my hand, she led me to a wall filled with ancient scrolls. She reached upwards and picked up a small scroll covered in dust and bound with a purple ribbon. Then, after running her hand over it to wipe away the dust, she opened it up and started to read.

"'It has been planned that the seed of this earth shall shift. The human race will grow in spirit and in love. A child will be born, who will be celebrated for centuries, not as a king nor a prince but as a common man who sacrificed his life so that we may enter the Kingdom of God. His death will not be forgotten, but the real shift will lie in the birth of another child. A secret child born in a distant land, protected by an army of princes. These princes will never know whom it is they protect, or why they must protect this child, but their hearts will be guided for eternity to do so.

"This child will be born a girl and her children and their children will prosper and grow, spreading the message of love and light. They will possess the inherent ability to open the hearts and minds of all they meet.

"The mother of this child will arrive in Alexandria. You will recognize her, for she will be disguised as an old, sick man who seeks a cure. Take her in, feed her, protect her, and in exchange she will tell you her story. You must protect this story from the hands of the greedy, from the false prophets. When it is safe, her story will be told.'"

I gazed up at her, tears pouring down my face. She looked back at me, placed her two hands on my stomach and said:

"Thank you for coming here. I promise to protect you."

Before I could ask her who had written this and what it all meant, three men burst into the library. Quickly, Ophelia placed her hands over my mouth and hid us from their sight.

The voices of the men echoed through the room. They

discussed a new prisoner who bore the mark of David. They were unsure if they could trust him and were looking to the library to guide them. I peeked over Ophelia's shoulder, attempting to glimpse the men as they argued about what to do, when suddenly I recognized one of the group as the young man who had tried to rape me. Without thinking, I gasped aloud, a sound that echoed throughout the room.

Abruptly, the men stopped speaking and looked in our direction.

"Ophelia, is that you? What are you doing here?" one of them asked.

Our presence could no longer be hidden and Ophelia sheepishly stepped forward into the light. "Yes, Father, it is I," she replied.

The man walked to us quickly, snatching the scroll from her hands before casting his eyes to me. He pulled me away from behind her and hastily dragged me to the centre of the room. I remained silent, unsure what was happening.

"You dare to jeopardize our people by bringing a complete stranger into the sacred library!" he bellowed.

His voice echoed throughout the room and, as intended, made me fearful. And just as he looked ready to continue on, his attention turned to the scroll in his hand, the one Ophelia had read to me from.

His stern appearance suddenly softened as he read the passage it was open to. Then, he looked straight into my eyes, placed his each hand on one of my shoulders and turned me around, inspecting every inch of me, before asking gently:

"Are you the one who was disguised as an old man and asleep outside in the Temple square last night?"

I remained quiet, but gently nodded my head.

He took my hand and softly kissed it, before turning to the others to say, "I think we have found our answer."

"Is it my brother of whom you speak?" I asked tentatively. "His name is Philip and I have not seen him since yesterday. Please tell me it is him and that he is safe."

"I do believe it is your brother, and I assure you he is and will be kept safe. I apologize for your distress. Tonight we will celebrate the arrival of you and your brother with a special dinner," announced Ophelia's father.

"Ophelia, thank you for bringing this to my attention. Now make sure our guest is well looked after, and that she has the appropriate attire for this evening's festivities."

Ophelia nodded to her father, keeping her head low as she gripped my arm and swiftly led me back towards the palace.

"I'm so sorry about my father. He is a kind man, I assure you," she told me, clearly embarrassed and perhaps even slightly fearful.

I could tell something big had just happened and that these men, while wise, possessed a strong and

God-fearing authority. In viewing how Ophelia had reacted to her father, I suspected he could be a hard and cruel man when necessary. This, however, did not bother me. I trusted him and I trusted my path, but above all, I was thrilled that Philip would be coming back to me.

The rest of the day passed quickly. Ophelia and her servants prepared a beautiful robe for me to wear at dinner, and although I was embarrassed at how big my belly had grown and was uncomfortable to show it, the dress — with its white under layer, beautiful red over layer and gold trimmings — made me feel like a queen, especially once I adorned my hair with the gold leaves Ophelia procured for me. She was so kind to me during the time I spent at the palace, and I thoroughly enjoyed being in the company of women once again. Ophelia reminded me of what it would be like to live with a sister. Perhaps our relationship was similar to what I would have had been with my own sisters had I never left Magdala for Jerusalem. Of course, I could never regret that choice as it had led me to Yeshua and blessed me with this growing being inside my belly, who without a doubt would bring endless joy to all those he or she met.

I spent most of the day reflecting upon where I was and from where I had come. The events that had just passed and those that took place in Jerusalem. I kindly asked one of the students to bring some ink and papyrus and I began to write. It felt good to put words to papyrus — as though recording the events of my life made them more real. No longer were they memories and emotions swirling in my mind, they became real, life-changing events that I had witnessed, lived, breathed, rejoiced and mourned.

In my writings, Yeshua was alive once again, as were Sara, Mary and my aunties. Their love, sacrifice, wisdom and generosity would no longer vanish in the dust of our past but would be recorded forever and kept safe in the sacred library of Alexandria. Generations to come would know that I sat there and told my story, that I shared the truth of the great man called Yeshua who left us too soon but gave us such hope.

He was a man who walked in the light of God. A man who acted as an example of our own individual potential, accessible to everyone when we surrender to the grace of God. He made us healers, forgave our sins, cured our minds from greed, our bodies from disease and souls from fear. He was a walking angel, yet no different from any of us. He didn't want to be the King of the Jews, nor a Messiah. He just wanted to give people the freedom to live in peace and harmony; to live up to our authentic and essential natures.

When he walked on water, he did not perform a miracle; he merely demonstrated that we are all but spiritual beings and so is the water, the ground, the trees and the rocks. If we connect with everything on a spiritual level, what is real becomes a miracle, and a miracle is only that which is real. He showed us that life without miracles is an illusion, marking us as slaves to our closed minds. But that with a glimpse of the love and power of God, we too can live a life full of miracles.

CHAPTER FIFTEEN

A Dinner With Kings

8: But if the Savior made her worthy, who are you indeed to reject her? Surely the Savior knows her very well.

9: That is why He loved her more than us. Rather let us be ashamed and put on the perfect Man, and separate as He commanded us and preach the gospel, not laying down any other rule or other law beyond what the Savior said.

10: And when they heard this they began to go forth to proclaim and to preach.[15]

— GOSPEL OF MARY

PHILIP WAS BROUGHT TO ME in the early afternoon and we embraced like we had months earlier after years apart.

---

[15] The Gospel According to Mary Magdalene, Chapter 9, http://gnosis.org/library/marygosp.htm.

He looked tired and strained and I could see in his eyes that he had passed a gruelling night.

"I am so sorry, Mariamne, I thought I had lost you," he said miserably, holding back his tears.

"It was my promise to keep you safe and I just left you. Please accept my apology. I will never leave your side again. I will enlist an army of soldiers to be forever at your service, to protect you, this child and all the future children to come. This is my final word."

"Oh, Philip, you are my brother and my blood, we can never be lost from each other. Our Lord is continually with us and has brought us back together in the company of these kind people, who I know will lead us to safety and freedom."

"I'm not as convinced that these people are our friends," replied Philip.

"Oh, you sound like Peter and Thomas combined," I laughed. I then begged him to wipe the sour look from his face and to trust these people.

Knowing that sometimes it is easier to surrender to your circumstances than fight your fears, Philip smiled and walked off with the other servants to his chambers so he too could prepare for dinner.

The sun was soon setting upon the palace, which was alive with activity. Hundreds of students were rushing around preparing for the evening's festivities, which felt too grandiose for my humble self and brother. But Ophelia's father had insisted we were to join them for dinner, and I had a feeling that it would be my moment to convince them to help us find safety. Only several days had passed since our brothers were being hunted by the Roman soldiers, and I could not forget that that included myself and Philip.

Already, I longed terribly for word from Jerusalem, but I would respect my orders not to send word until we had arrived on safe land. I had promised this to Joseph and Mary, and I would not go back on my words as I knew we were still in danger. I prayed each night for their protection and somewhere deep in my heart I felt that everything was to work out as it was destined.

After completing the final touches on myself for dinner, I pulled out the necklace Yeshua had left me and re-read his letter. I placed the chain around my neck with the pendant sitting comfortably against my heart. Tonight, my dear Yeshua would be with me, giving me the courage to face whatever it was that awaited me.

When Philip returned to my room, my, did he look handsome. I had never seen him dressed so formally, in robes a soft golden colour with royal blue trimmings. He gave me a smile and shrugged awkwardly in his new clothing, which was not only unfamiliar to him but appeared mildly restricting.

He took my hand, and together, in silence, we followed one of the students through the palace to the great dining hall.

When we arrived, I was shocked to see that there were at least 200 guests present. It seemed that all the prefects and councilmen of Alexandria were there with their wives and eldest children. We were led to our dinner places and it quickly became apparent that the dinner was not for us at all, we were simple guests who almost vanished amongst the crowd of powerful men.

Ophelia came to us, looking radiant in a long purple robe trimmed with gold leafing, gold leaves adorning her hair as they did mine. She squeezed my hand and whispered into my ear.

"My darling Mariamne, I may not be able to spend much time with you this evening, but please enjoy yourself and relax. You and your brother will be well looked after, that I promise."

With those words she gracefully walked across the room to sit by her father near the head of the table. Everyone was soon seated, though I noticed that there remained an empty seat at the head of the table. I wondered who might be missing — perhaps a family member I had yet to meet?

My question was answered when an army of Roman soldiers marched abruptly through the entrance to the hall. I felt Philip automatically stiffen next to me, and I knew he was surely feeling the same grave concern as I. Under the table, I squeezed his hand as I gave him a reassuring look, hoping to convey that everything would be okay. Although my heart was pounding, a sense of calm had settled over me and I knew Yeshua was sitting there with me. I knew he would protect us.

The soldiers parted and through them entered a man of distinct power and authority, dressed in the robes of an emperor. I leaned over to Philip and ever so quietly asked, "Who is he?"

"Tiberius Caesar, the emperor of Rome," whispered Philip. Though I had no formal opinion of the man, just the sound of his name caused a cold shiver to run down my spine. Squeezing Philip's hand again, I said a little prayer to our Father and protectors, asking that our presence go unnoticed during the evening's reception.

Once Tiberius Caesar was seated at the head of the table, the true festivities began with an abundance of food pouring out of the kitchens and filling the tables. The emperor seemed like a jovial man and spent most of the night telling stories, some without much meaning and others clearly embellishing his conquests of Pannonia, Dalmatia and Raetia. At the end of each story the room would explode with cheering and everyone would raise their glasses to the great emperor. Truly, it became quite tiresome.

As dinner neared its conclusion, a Roman soldier approached Tiberius and passed him a note. The room fell silent as everyone watched him read it before he cleared his throat and slowly stood up.

"Aulus Avilius Flaccus, I must firstly thank you for tonight's reception and your continued dedication to Rome. This evening is a great display of what a virtuous Prefect you are and what great achievements will come. It has come to my attention, however, that amongst your guests are two traitors of Rome whom we must arrest accordingly. I apologise for the disturbance, and you have my word that my soldiers will proceed swiftly so as not to dampen the joy of this evening's success."

Before Tiberius even had a chance to nod to his soldiers, I rose to my feet. All eyes instantly turned to me.

"My emperor, is it the presence of my brother and I of which you speak?"

I stood there boldly and bravely, while Philip stared at me in disbelief, whether it was for my arrogance in addressing the emperor, for giving up our presence so easily, or both, I did not know. But I did not care. I could see Ophelia sitting close to Tiberius and she smiled in my direction, as though she believed I was doing the right thing. Her strength and solidarity gave me the courage to follow through with what I had initiated. Her father, on the other hand, had turned a pale shade of white, for I suspected not even he could protect me in this situation, though his scriptures had called for it.

Within seconds several Roman soldiers appeared at our sides. I remained standing and so did Tiberius, who appeared almost impressed by my naive, yet daring confrontation.

"And what is your name, young lady?" Tiberius asked me.

"My name is Mariamne and I come from Magdala," I declared, looking him in the eye.

"And is it you who took house and company amongst the now executed, so-called King of the Jews, Yeshua?"

"Yes," I replied, shaky now.

Without another word Tiberius gave the soldiers a nod and they swiftly took hold of my arms, gripping them firmly.

"But he is not dead," I insisted, never taking my eyes off the emperor.

Appearing humoured by my brazenness, he motioned to the soldiers to let me go.

"Let us hear from you about your so-called King of the Jews, who is apparently still alive," laughed Tiberius. Most of those in the room broke into laughter, giving me a moment to compose myself.

"Firstly, he was not the King of the Jews. The High Priests poisoned Pontious Pilate into believing this tale so that he would be arrested. It was the High Priests of the Jews who wanted him dead, because he spoke the truth about their God and unveiled their corrupt and misguided ways. But this is just a divergence, he was a great man who did great things. And he has risen."

"I do not believe you. No one can rise from the dead, not even the greatest of emperors. It is impossible, just as it is for these white eggs to turn red," Tiberius laughed as he gestured towards the eggs at the centre of the table.

I leaned forward and picked up the whitest of the eggs that were resting in front of me. I held the egg between my thumb and my middle finger, up high so everyone could see. There were gasps around the room as it turned from white to red in my fingers.

"Yeshua is alive and my brother and I must remain free persons, so we can share the truth of his story," I concluded.

Tiberius didn't take his eyes off me, though he dared me to do it again. Keeping my eyes on him, I picked up another egg, turning it red. I then picked up the entire basket of eggs in front of me, held it high for all to see, as they too turned a bright red.

"I ask everyone to look to your tables. Not only will you see that my eggs have turned red, but so too has every other egg in this room. Yeshua is alive! As a man of your word, Emperor, I trust that you will honour our liberties and freedom. We are humble countrymen who respect the laws of Rome and pay our taxes. We just happened to meet an extraordinary man along the way called Yeshua. I have no doubt that one day all of the Roman Kingdom will learn the truth of who he was, and they too will enjoy the glories of the Kingdom of Heaven."

Appearing utterly astonished, Tiberius broke the thick silence of the room by clapping his hands together, and before I knew it the others in the room had also erupted into applause.

"My soldiers will escort you and your brother to wherever you wish to travel. They will protect and provide for you, on one condition. Once you have your baby and you are settled, you come visit me in Rome."

I nodded, smiled at the emperor and then returned to my seat without another word.

CHAPTER SIXTEEN

A Story in Exchange for Safety

> *"So it is with realized Human Beings, who work with energies*
> *that obey them. They prepare all things to come into being.*
> *Thus everything awakens, and is redeemed: good and evil, right*
> *and left. The Breath leads all things to their repose, it aligns*
> *the energies: the obedient, the wild, and the solitary ones. It*
> *gathers them together, so that they are no longer dispersed.*
>
> *41: The created one is beautiful, and his sons are noble."*[16]
>
> — GOSPEL OF PHILIP

THE NEXT MORNING at breakfast, Ophelia's father joined
me and asked to share some words in private. He was
not thrilled about my bold approach with the emperor
but was relieved that his house remained intact and

---

[16] The Gospel of Philip, Page 6, Plate 108, Translated by Jean-Yves Leloup,
Inner Traditions 2004, p.71.

that he could provide the safety his scriptures had assigned him. My display at the dinner had gone far to fully convince him that I truly was the one spoken of in the texts, and he gave me his honest word that he would see to it that Philip, myself and my unborn child would arrive safely in a place where I would be able to start my new life without threat nor fear.

This protection would not come without a price. While I was to stay in the palace to be cared for by their midwives until my baby arrived, I was also expected to record all that I knew of Yeshua and the time that we had passed together. In exchange for our freedom, my story would remain in the great library of Alexandria. It appeared to be a barter, but I was humbled by the great Prefect's gesture and graciously accepted his kind offer.

Over the next weeks I spent my days with a kind scribe called Dominus, who wrote all that I recanted. Philip also took the opportunity to continue his writings, which he had started back in Jerusalem. So that our stories could also travel with us to our new home, Philip recorded all that I told Dominus, in addition to his own experiences with Yeshua. When he was not keeping records with us, he would practice-fight with the king's soldiers. He was determined to protect me and, although I had great faith in what was to unfold, Philip did not trust the word of the palace nor that of Tiberius.

While Philip mastered his swordsman skills, I passed my afternoons with the women and midwives. They would perform sacred ceremonies and prayers for the safe arrival of my child. I also spent time teaching them my healing secrets, and showed them how Yeshua had taught us to heal the sick, the blind and the lonely. Because we shared our secrets and practiced on one another each day, our strength and energy were strong. Our healing became powerful, and by the time I departed, there was not a woman in the palace who did not feel confident that they too could heal themselves and those they encountered.

Every morning at the break of dawn we would come together in what we called the sacred circle. Only the women of the palace were privy to the event, so Ophelia, the great midwives and the girls who trained beneath us would gather. One by one we would enter the oval chapel and silently take our seats in the circle. Once everyone was seated, we would hold hands and begin to hum, feeling the vibrations of our voices and the healing energy of our souls pass through our hands, moving fluidly from one to the other.

After some time passed, the women would rise to their feet and guide me to the centre of the circle. I would lay down on my back with the women surrounding me, then, each would place their hands on my body, in accordance with my teachings. Perhaps twelve pairs of hands lay gently across my body, placed on my head, my arms, my heart, my belly, my hips, my legs and my feet. I could feel the soft, warm, loving, healing energy flow from their palms to each and every cell of my body. I would close my eyes and see a soft golden light pouring down from the heavens, healing my heart, my sadness and grief, while also nurturing my unborn child.

It was in this space that I'd find Yeshua. I would be able to see his face again, feel him close to me. It was as if he was a lighter version of himself, free from the burdens and stresses he was used to carrying with him. His face was soft and his eyes filled with love and grace. I could see and feel him as he placed his hands on my belly and whispered to our child.

It's hard to describe the type of plane I would enter when I saw my Yeshua, but it was as if I could see between two parallel worlds. The real, tangible world, where the women surrounded me; and this other world, almost like a window or passageway to another field. The energy and vibrations in this field were lighter and it was through the vibrational passageway that healing energy would travel from God, down to us and through to the worldly plane.

Just a few minutes in this space could feel like an eternity and other times hours could feel like fleeting minutes. It was a space where time truly did not exist, where anything and everything was possible.

Looking back, I am deeply grateful I had time to heal

my heavy heart before my child was born. I had time to sit and be with women who nurtured me and helped me gain courage for the next chapter of my life. Time to share my, and Yeshua's, teachings and blessings. I was thankful for the time to reflect, time to sleep, time to cry, time to rejoice and time to simply be.

CHAPTER SEVENTEEN

The Midnight Escape

MY CHILD WAS EXPECTED in autumn, and leading up to that time, the women of the household stayed diligent in their duties to protect me and nurture my body. As agreed, mine and Philip's safety were guaranteed in exchange for our stories and writings. We stayed true to this agreement and remained ever so grateful for the hospitality those in the great palace offered us.

Everything changed one evening when, during the darkest hours of night as the entire household slept, Philip came to my side and woke me.

"Mariamne, we must go. We are no longer safe. Aulus's spies have heard word that Tiberius has changed his attitude and does not wish to keep his agreement to allow us safe passage. The Prefect has arranged for us to leave tonight by boat."

Confused and still half asleep, I raised my head from my warm bedding and looked into Philip's eyes. His hands were shaking and I could see him trying to fight back his fear. I took a moment to centre my energy and check in with my heart and my mind. I sensed that what Philip was saying was true and we were indeed no longer safe in Alexandria.

I quickly packed the few belongings I had brought with me and prepared to leave. As I turned to go, I found Ophelia and Sarah, a young servant girl, waiting for me at the entrance.

"Oh, Mariamne, how much you have enriched our lives by being with us. I am so blessed to have met you and I promise we will continue to protect your story and practice your healings."

"Thank you my dear Ophelia," I replied graciously as I leaned forward to embrace her.

"You are my true sister and I will always think of you. You will be in my prayers and I bless you with protection for all that you have done and sacrificed for us."

"I have packed some things for your journey, and all that you will need for the arrival of your baby. I am also gifting you Sarah. She has been by my side since she was born and I know she will be loyal to you and serve you well," continued Ophelia.

With tears streaming down my face, I embraced her one last time. I could feel her heart, her love and her compassion vibrating through me. She was a special soul and I knew that, somehow, we would meet again. Our souls were destined to cross paths; if not again in this lifetime, surely in the next.

"I love you, Ophelia. Stay safe, stay true and stay strong."

And with those words I clasped onto Sarah's tiny trembling hand and we both followed Philip out into the dead of night.

We walked through town without seeing a single soul. The night was crisp and clear and although we were fleeing, I felt more alive and at peace than I had in a long time. It was almost as if my life was playing out before me, and I was merely an observer who watched us walk silently across the emptied city square, through the hushed and sleeping market stalls, and finally to the deserted port. The boats were gently rising and falling, swaying in rhythm with the gentle waves that rocked beneath them. A single lamp held by Christopher, one of Aulus's guards, made it clear which boat was waiting for us. Christopher's wife, Mary, sat patiently in the darkness, greeting us with a welcoming smile and blankets for all. I sensed her internal fear and could see how relieved she was that we had made it to them safely.

After Sarah, Philip and myself climbed onto the vessel, Christopher unhooked the ropes and gently pushed our boat from the peer. He blew out the lamp and took charge of the boat's oars and sails. Our silence was a harmonious mantra, honouring our escape, honouring the journey we had taken thus far and uniting the five of us by embracing what destiny had foreordained.

In Alexandria, we left behind our comforts. We said goodbye to our friends, and we gave thanks for the time to rest and restore our faith. As we sailed away from our stories and the sacred words of Yeshua, both written and handed down, we took our attention to the stars, which would become our navigators and guides for the following weeks. We embraced the future, putting all fears and doubts aside, for we had already lived the worst. We knew that what was to come could only bring hope for a better world, a world that would soon know of Yeshua and his great capacity to love and heal. The same inherent gift that each of us harbours deep within our souls, just waiting for someone to come along and ignite its fire. Giving light to our natural greatness and birth to everyday miracles.

I revelled in the knowledge that the birth of my baby on new land would bring new beginnings, new dreams, new friendships and new opportunities to heal. Heal ourselves, heal our pasts and heal the future. Heal the blessed beings amongst us and align our hearts with God. His light was still burning inside of me, I could feel the flame flickering softly, waiting for the right moment to burst out of my chest and ignite the hearts of suffering souls. I took a moment to close my eyes and feel His love. His all-protecting and everlasting goodness, which would lead us to a welcoming land. A land that would not be afraid of God's word. A land that would shelter and provide for us until we were blessed with old age and all the wisdom that comes with time.

As I sat in that boat, contemplating all that was to come, I held tight to Sarah's hand. I knew she was scared and sad. And I knew she would never tell me. So, I gave her comfort through touch, my other hand rested on my belly. I imagined Yeshua sitting with us on the boat. Whispering to Christopher the perfect route, commanding the stars to shine brighter than ever before. Just being with us, travelling with us, telling us stories to raise our spirits and inspire our courage. I imagined how he would sing to our baby and I allowed his tune to softly soothe her. Her, my baby girl. It was in that very moment I was certain she would be a girl. My blessing, my love.

It would take us several weeks to arrive at our destination by boat, and we spent the time getting to know each other, telling stories of what we thought the land would be like when we arrived. We fantasised about living on a small island that would be invisible to the Romans and plentiful with fruit and grains. An island with soft sandy beaches, lush green hills and an abundance of fish and sweet gifts from the sea. New and exotic plants and herbs that would provide us with effective cures and fresh spices for our kitchens. The hum of children singing and playing freely in the gardens. A whisper of Temple bells from a distance, from a land we could no longer see and from which we were kept forever safe and protected.

Christopher and Philip would, of course, excite heated arguments about what to do with our invisible island once it was invaded by the Romans. The men did not have much patience for fantasy, and preferred to focus and map out strategies for war and violence. Although it was with good intentions, I had no interest in listening to or thinking about fighting, death or destruction. They did not hold a place in my soul and I no longer had the patience to indulge in their ideologies. Instead, I took those moments to rest.

One afternoon on our journey, there was a story that would engage every bit of my attention. It was late afternoon and we had passed a lovely warm day sailing the seas; the men had had success at catching fish and Mary was busy cleaning the flesh and salting them, letting them dry out under the sun. Despite the merry spirit on the boat at the thought of our next meal, Philip sat staring out across the horizon, chipping away with a knife at a wooden stump he'd begun carving the same day we departed on our boat journey.

"My sister," Philip said, hardly looking at me. "I must tell you something. I can no longer keep it inside and, although I was sworn to secrecy, I feel it is only right that you should know."

Having caught my full attention, I turned to him.

"What is it, my brother? I can see something has been

weighing heavy on your brow. Please don't be afraid, you cannot do me harm. I am your sister and I will always love you."

"Yeshua was your husband and thus you have the right to know," said Philip, determined. Then, "We stole his body."

I stared back at him blankly, not knowing how to reply but also not wanting him to stop revealing his truth.

"On the Friday after his death, the Roman soldier who had befriended you delivered us Yeshua's body as promised. We brought him safely to the tomb where he was to be laid to rest and we rolled a large stone in front of the entrance to prevent anyone from entering. However, the next afternoon rumors were already travelling through Jerusalem. Matthew had overhead that the Roman soldiers were planning to steal Yeshua's body and burn it. They were fighting over who would go to the tomb and gambled over who would attain his powers.

"Mariamne, we were so afraid that they would find him. James, Matthew and I crafted a plan: Lazarus had a family tomb and we knew it would be safe to bury him there. It was the night of the Sabbath, and I know we have sinned for it. I have asked God for my penance, but we simply could not have let anything happen to Yeshua's body. Dressed as farmers, we crept in to retrieve his remains in the dead of night. Then, we laid his body over a donkey and covered him with branches of palm. If anyone saw us, we simply looked like poor old shepherds moving material to build our sleeping spot for the night. Though no one asked us or even looked in our direction. We led the donkey to Lazarus' tomb and laid him safely to rest."

I stared back at Philip, a single tear running down my cheek.

"Mariamne, the other disciples do not know either, we kept it a secret from everyone, not just you. Except, I did send word to our aunties. I sent Simon, the son of Matteus, to go to our aunties and tell them. They would have anointed his body as it is so deserved. Simon would have been faithful, I am sure of it.

"Please forgive me. This does not take away the importance that although you did not find Yeshua in the tomb, he found you. He came to you, He spoke to you, He is alive and continues to live with you," concluded Philip.

I was confused, saddened and relieved all at the same time. I didn't truly know what to think of it all, but I was comforted to know that his body was safe.

"Thank you, my brother, you truly are a great person. I am humbled that you shared this story with me and grateful for the sacrifice and effort you took to save his body. I will never forget that, and I honour you for your bravery and loyalty. Yes, I am his wife, but you are and have always been his most loyal disciple and friend.

Thank you," I said simply before I turned away to look out across the sea.

The others remained silent, continuing their work as if they had heard nothing. Sarah, though, came to my side and laid her sweet head in my lap. I gently caressed her hair and took comfort in her presence.

Philip's story had reminded me of my heartache at not having been given the opportunity to anoint Yeshua. I understood my emotions and lamentations to be childish indulgences, and I knew Philip had shared with me some positive news, but still I could not help but feel slightly betrayed and sad. I allowed myself to wallow, as it somehow soothed me; though, after some time, I accepted that although Philip's confession had reminded me of my great pain, it had also reminded me of great love and learning. The greater the pain, the greater the love, and I am thus grateful to have loved and have been loved by Yeshua.

CHAPTER EIGHTEEN

A Storm and a Birth

"If you bring forth what is within you, what you bring forth will save you. If you do not bring forth what is within you, what you do not bring forth will destroy you."

— GOSPEL OF THOMAS[17]

OUR JOURNEY BY SEA was relatively uneventful. The days were usually filled with sunshine and God blessed us with strong winds. We each found our daily routine; time to work together; time to pass the time with stories and time to contemplate the future in solace.

One particular day at sea, I was feeling much more lethargic than usual and took the liberty to rest whenever I could. I found myself a nice spot to sleep in the shade of the sails and asked Sarah to join me. My belly was

---

17 https://www.goodreads.com/quotes/126072-if-you-bring-forth-what-is-within-you-what-you.

big and awkward, and had started to feel heavy. I asked Sarah to place her hands on my abdomen and pray for me as I rested. This was uncommon, though perhaps it was my mother's instincts — I could sense that something important was waiting for us around the corner.

The warmth of Sarah's hands on my belly was comforting. I closed my eyes, surrendered my thoughts and allowed myself to fall into a deep sleep, where my dreams escorted me on a beautiful journey back in time to Yeshua's and my wedding day. I could see and feel the golden light that kissed our faces as we stood in front of one another, declaring our love to God and uniting our souls for eternity. I could smell Yeshua, and feel his touch, his warmth, his embrace, his kiss. I was finally home again. Only the two of us existed, breathing in unison, merging into each other. My heart felt full, so content and bursting with joy.

In my dream, Yeshua held my hand and asked me to go for a walk with him, away from our friends and family. As we walked along the river's edge, he told me how proud he was of me, and how proud he was when I stood up to Tiberius. He recalled everything that had transpired since his death, confirming that he was still so very close to me. I longed to stay in that dream space forever, to simply forget about all that had transpired. Forget about our exile and return to our matrimonial bliss. The bliss that had been fleeting, but had conceived the gift from God growing inside of me. The spark of God and our love gave life to a new being, and although she would never meet her father, there would not pass a single day without me telling her about him and his greatness.

"Mariamne, Mariamne, look at me," said Yeshua in my dream. "I have something very important to tell you and there isn't much time. You must pay attention."

Bringing my full attention back to the presence of Yeshua, I listened intently.

"There is no longer time, a storm is coming. It is not going to be easy and it will most likely be terrifying. Trust in the hand of God, that He will bring you all to safety. I am with you. You will be safe and so will our brothers and sisters. But there is something you must do. You must turn the boat around. Christopher will disagree with you and so will Philip. They are strong, fearless men, and they will want to face the storm head on. You must do whatever it is that you need to to make them listen to you. You *must* turn the boat around."

"Mariamne, Mariamne! Wake up, wake up!"

I jolted out of my dream state by Sarah shaking my shoulders and calling my name.

"There is a storm coming, we must get you under cover," Sarah told me.

In disbelief, I turned towards the bow of the boat, watching as the waves rose higher and higher, and large dark gray clouds rushed towards us. The winds had picked up considerably and we were heading straight into what looked like the eye of the storm.

Philip quickly grasped my arm and placed me next to Mary and Sarah at the stern. He dressed us warmly, covering us in blankets and placing a series of sails around us to shield us from the winds. The rain started to pour down, every drop hitting us with more force than the previous one. The wind blew heavier, forcing the rain into our faces, and whipping our cheeks like lashes of ice.

"Philip, Philip, you have to listen to me," I yelled towards him. "We must turn the boat around." But I could see that he did not hear me as he worked to help Christopher control the vessel.

"Philip!" I screamed. "We must turn the boat around."

But still, nothing. Sarah looked at me, terrified, and Mary held on to me, trying to hide her own fear by comforting me.

I turned to Sarah. "Listen, I know you are scared, but trust me, we will be okay. Yeshua came to me just now in a dream, and he told me this would happen. He promised we would be safe, that God will guide us to safety. But we *must* turn the boat around."

Giving her an imploring look, I begged of her, "Go to Philip and tell him that I have started to bleed. That we must turn the boat around. Tell him what I just told you. Be brave, you can do this."

At my words, Sarah looked directly at me, her face having changed from a scared little girl to a fierce woman.

"But, Mariamne, it is true. Look, you are bleeding," replied Sarah.

I looked down and saw that she was right, a small stream of blood had started to flow down my leg. Without hesitating, Sarah stood and used all her strength to move towards Philip, holding onto the sturdy wooden beams of our vessel to guide her and support her on her mission. I saw her approach Philip and yell into his ear. I saw Philip look at me and then look back at the storm. Just for a moment he hesitated, as if all of his instincts were telling him to keep going ahead. But then he seemed to remember his promise to protect his sister and her baby.

He swiftly seized Sarah and brought her back to me, his strong arms embracing her and protecting her from the waves that were now belting across the boat. He placed her next to me and with no time to say a word marched back to the rudder, yelling at Christopher to turn the boat around and change the mast. Christopher appeared to insist we keep moving forward, but when he saw the look in Philip's eye, he rose to his feet and changed the direction of the sails. Philip helped guide the boat around and in a few moments we were moving away from the storm.

Not knowing where we were headed or what we were going to encounter, the men gave their hearts and courage over to faith, focusing only on guiding us out of the storm.

After what felt like an eternity, the clouds began to lighten and the rain eased off. Small rays of sunshine began to peek through the clouds and, as if it were a mirage, land appeared before us. We looked at each other with utter disbelief. A single tear of gratitude rolled down Philip's cheek, and it was clear he could no longer hold up his armour against the rush of emotions that came with our survival of the storm. Christopher turned to Philip and embraced him firmly, as they both celebrated their moment of triumph.

During the peak of the storm, the dark clouds had hidden the land from our vision and we had sailed right past the island. As the men steered the boat towards the newfoundland, a wave of relief washed over all of us and lifted our spirits.

"Thank you, Yeshua," I whispered to myself.

Within moments of turning the boat in the direction of land I started to feel a strong sensation in my belly. I screamed in pain as the intensity caught me by surprise. My first contractions had begun and although I had witnessed hundreds of births, had held the hands of hundreds of women as they cried out in agony, I'd had no real understanding of such pain until that moment.

Sarah held my hand and Mary rushed to my side, instinctively rubbing my lower back. The two women breathed with me and squeezed my hands with every contraction. I surrendered myself to their care, breathing with them, and allowing the pain to strangle my womb when it needed to. Giving myself the freedom to vocalise the pain as I felt necessary.

Philip and Christopher brought the boat quickly to shore and carried me over the rocks to a small clearing. The women followed with blankets and made a humble space out of nothing. They ordered the men to leave; to start a fire for us and catch some fish for supper.

I placed myself on my hands and knees and commenced rocking back and forth, gently. With Mary rubbing my back and Sarah coaching me through my breathing, it felt as though the three of us were giving birth together, and I was grateful for their presence. They gave me strength and they held me when I needed it most.

As the contractions became stronger and more intense, I closed my eyes and listened to my body. I surrendered to it and allowed it to do what it was made to do. With every contraction I closed my eyes and could see and feel the presence of all my female ancestors who had crossed over. They too gathered to assist in the birth of my child, giving me an unimaginable amount of strength and force that unquestionably helped me birth my baby into the world.

I don't know how long we were there together, breathing, screaming, crying and even laughing at times. But finally my body began to push. The agony of the contractions was overwhelming and every instinct of my body was telling me to stop. I was exhausted and afraid, and I feared I did not have the strength to finish what I had begun.

Looking towards Sarah and Mary, I cried, "I can't. I can't do this, it's too much." But the women just smiled and looked at me with love and faith.

"Mariamne, you were born to do this. You have come so far and it will be over in a matter of moments now. Release your fears to God, breathe and all you need to do is push," said Mary, gripping my hand and looking deeply into my eyes.

And right there in that moment, I could feel all my ancestors passing to me an inexplicable amount of courage and power. I closed my eyes and drew in their energy, energy that gave me the strength to push one last time, finally bringing my baby girl into this world.

Mary carefully held her tiny little body within her arms and brought her to me. Resting her on my chest, we stared into each other's eyes for the first time. She had his eyes; my baby girl had Yeshua's eyes. An overwhelming sense of relief and joy and love came rushing over me all at once. I held my baby girl and she looked back at me, mouth open and crying. I caressed her ever so gently, and as I started to talk to her, her cries stopped. She looked up at me as if she knew me.

"Yes, baby girl, welcome. We've been waiting for you," I whispered to her softly.

Philip returned then, his eyes filled with tears. He was a strong man and rarely showed his emotions, though I suspected, as he stood before me sobbing like a small child, the combination of stress from the storm and the adrenalin of the birth had somehow broken his shield. In that moment, he was so like the small brother I remembered falling and cutting open his knees. His armour had softened and he too surrendered to the beauty of this precious baby girl who rested in my arms.

"Her name is Mary," I said, turning to Philip. "I want her to be named after Yeshua's mother. She has his eyes and she too will live on in honour of him."

"That is the perfect name for her. Well done, my sweet sister," replied Philip, kissing me on the forehead.

"We have prepared a fire and found a perfect place to rest. There doesn't appear to be any locals on the island, so we can rest for a few days and restore our energy."

"Thank you, Philip, I am so blessed to have you by my side through all of this," I said gratefully.

We did as Philip suggested and regrouped for the next few days on the island. The men fished and the women gathered fruits and seeds. All the while I sat with my sweet baby girl. We got to know each other as I fed her, cuddled her, sang to her and nurtured her through her first days in this world.

CHAPTER NINETEEN

Salvation

> *Jesus says:*
>
> *1: "I am the light that is over all. I am the All.*
> *The All came forth out of me. And to me the All has come."*
> *2: "Split a piece of wood – I am there.*
> *3: Lift the stone, and you will find me there"*[18]
>
> — THE GOSPEL OF THOMAS

AFTER A FEW DAYS on the island we set sail in our battled vessel, headed towards what we hoped would be our final destination. The sails were broken from the storm and the ship was not in the best of conditions, but none of us questioned the journey. We knew we were being guided and we knew deep in our hearts that wherever

---

[18] The Gospel of Thomas Translated by Stephen J. Patterson and James M. Robinson, Chapter 77, http://gnosis.org/naghamm/gth_pat_rob.htm.

we were heading was where our destiny lay. God was guiding us there and we were simply present to His plan.

Fortuitously, the remainder of our journey was kind to us, and it did not take us long to reach our final destination. Despite our lack of sails, after three days at sea we arrived at safe lands, on a small beach in Arelate in Gallia.

As our vessel approached the vast sandy seashore, a few of the locals gathered on the beach to greet us. They looked incredulous, as though they could not believe it possible that our storm-wrecked vessel had been able to hold together and bring us to safety on their beach.

As I took my first steps onto the sacred ground of Arelate, I knew we were home. I knew deep within my soul that that was the place I needed to be and that my daughter would be safe there.

As I took off my sandals and dug my feet into the warm, sun-kissed sand, it was as if the earth were talking to me through the soles of my feet, whispering "welcome home" through every single grain of the soft sands. A warm embracing sensation rose through my body, gifting me with a sense of deep inner knowing. I turned to Sarah, who was standing next to me and beaming with the biggest smile of happiness and relief. I gently handed baby Mary to her and, remembering Joseph's request to bless the land once we arrived, I knelt down to my knees and bent over, placing my palms on the sandy granules that made up the land we stood upon. I then rested my head just above my hands, and bowed to the earth. I whispered to the soft sands, sending my prayers through each grain and then even deeper into the centre of the earth. I thanked the earth for its hospitality, abundance and for welcoming us home. I breathed in the sweet new air and then, looking up towards the sky, I opened my arms and palms towards the clouds and continued my prayer:

"Thank You, Lord, for bringing us to this precious corner of Your world. Bless this land we walk upon and its people. May the earth be blessed with prosperous crops and may its people be blessed with good fortune, safety, freedom and health. We are Your humble servants and are forever grateful for Your unfailing guidance and protection."

With that being said, I rose to my feet and smiled in the direction of the locals who had come to our assistance. They welcomed us into their village with open arms and over the coming days, weeks and months, we would truly find ourselves at home.

It did not take us long to settle into our new surroundings and I soon found that my days as a new mother became easier. Mary grew bigger and stronger with each passing moment and her cheeks started to fill out with rosy blessings on them.

As Mary grew in size and character, I was able to

spend more time with the locals, listening to them, witnessing their lives and just being present. I did not want to invade what they had already created, and I wanted them to know that they could trust us.

On one particular morning, when Mary was about four months old, I left her with Sarah so I could spend the day with our new neighbours. I had befriended a lovely elder woman called Joan, who would share with me the history of their town and describe to me all the different families and characters that lived there. She made me laugh, and for reasons unknown to myself, I always felt safe around her. So I asked her if there was someone I could trust to send a letter to Bethlehem. She simply looked at me curiously, took my hand and led me towards a small house at the corner of the village.

As we entered the home, I was surprised to see it filled with young men, seemingly preparing for a voyage.

Joan introduced me to the men and asked if we could have a private word with Matteus. A young fair-haired man rose to his feet and guided us to the adjacent room.

"Hello, Matteus, my name is Mariamne and I am pleased to meet you," I said, opening my hands towards him.

Without taking my hand, he looked deep into my eyes and replied:

"I know who you are. You have visited me in my dreams over the past several months. I am not sure why it is I whom you have chosen, but I am honoured to oblige your every request."

He then took my hand, kissed it and knelt to his knees.

"I know who you are and I know that the angels are surrounding you. I have seen them, such bright, lighted creatures. My only hope is that if I help you, the same angels will keep me and my men safe along our journey. Tomorrow we leave for Rome, with hopes of employment with the emperor," he continued.

"My dear sweet Matteus, I have no doubt that the angels will be with you, and I will pray to our heavenly Father that your journey may be kind, safe and full of blessings," I said.

"I have a letter that I wish for you to deliver, in any matter you see fit. It is for a dear friend in Bethlehem. I trust you with this task and bless you for your sincerity and bravery. I have no doubt your future will be long and prosperous," I finished.

I handed him the letter and he took it, smiling at me with pride, courage and assurance. Both Joan and I were turning to leave, when Matteus called out to us.

"Wait, please, I beg of you," he said. "Mariamne, please share your gift with us and bless my soldiers. I have heard of your prayer circles and the miracles you can perform. All that I ask in return for my help is that you spend a moment with my men. They are young and enthusiastic, but I also know the power of fear and how it can cripple an army of soldiers into the dead."

I smiled and nodded to Matteus, welcoming the opportunity to share the wisdom of God and His love and protection.

Matteus drew the attention of those in the room, gathering them together. He introduced me, before taking a step back and allowing me full rein.

I welcomed the men and asked them to lower their heads and place their right hands over the centres of their chests. To prepare themselves to receive and be initiated into the Kingdom of God.

I opened the prayer by raising my arms and moving my face towards the heavens, calling upon Yeshua, the angels and all of God's assistants, those in this world and those who had already crossed over. I asked for their presence and divine guidance. I then proceeded to walk around the room, placing my hands above the shoulders of each soldier, one by one, and allowing the holy spirit to come through me and bless them. Breathing in a golden light, I endowed each man with the great healing light energy, which would serve to protect and guide them.

The men were gracious and humbled by my gesture, and each individually thanked me for my time. I bowed down to each of them, to their greatness and their divine connection, which would guide them along their journey. With my task complete, Joan and I returned to our respective homes.

As I walked towards home, an overflowing sense of joy and love poured into my heart. I was relieved to have found the perfect candidate to safely deliver my letter to Mary and Joseph in Bethlehem. I had spent the past weeks writing down everything that had happened to us, and I wanted them to hear word of our journey, the wonderful news of the safe arrival of their beautiful granddaughter and how happy we were to be welcomed and embraced in our new home.

I often prayed for Mary and Joseph and longed to receive word that they were safe and well. I wondered how Mary was doing, whether she struggled as much as I did with the passing of Yeshua. He had left such a gaping hole in our worlds, and I prayed that her pain would heal and be replaced with a deeper sense of forgiveness, love and knowing.

I myself suffered many days when the pain and immense loss would overwhelm me and consume my every thought. During these days I would be haunted by the torturous images of Yeshua's crucifixion, unable to remove them from my mind. Thankfully, I had been blessed with our healthy, precious baby girl, Mary. Her presence always brought me back to the present and the joy of the moment, helping to gently heal the gaping wounds of the past, slowly but surely turning them into soft, lingering scars. Forever present, as a gentle reminder of the boundless love that we had shared and witnessed.

I could not explain how or why, but it was as if my meeting with Matteus had caused something deep within the consciousness of the town to shift. After that day, the locals seemed to embrace me more and more each day, often introducing themselves and asking me to join them for a meal.

Recognising this shift and sensing the trust that was bestowed upon me, I finally felt that the timing was right to start sharing our story and our truth with the people of Gallia. We began to gather with the local people in public, recounting the stories of Yeshua, and offering our gifts of prayer and healing. Unsurprisingly, the more we shared our experiences and the events of Yeshua's life, the more the people engaged with us. I sense that we had evoked a hunger to learn within the community. So it was at this time that we — Philip, Mary, Christopher, Sarah and myself — recommenced our devotion to the Divine, like Philip and I had always practised in Jerusalem. We welcomed those who wished to join us and invited those who needed healings to come forward to receive, free of charge and free of all judgements.

This was the very beginning of my ministry. We called it the Ministry of the Rosicrucian, in honour of the unwavering faith Yeshua had in me and the symbolic pendant he'd gifted me in his final days.

I was finally at home in my ministry and my heart sang with so much joy at being alive and able to share all that I had witnessed, loved and learnt.

CHAPTER TWENTY

The New Church

Jesus says:

1: "If those who lead you say to you: 'Look, the kingdom is in the sky!' then the birds of the sky will precede you.

2: If they say to you: 'It is in the sea,' then the fishes will precede you.

3: Rather, the kingdom is inside of you, and outside of you."

4: "When you come to know yourselves, then you will be known, and you will realize that you are the children of the living Father.

5: But if you do not come to know yourselves, then you exist in poverty, and you are poverty."

— GOSPEL OF THOMAS[19]

---

19 The Gospel of Thomas Translated by Stephen J. Patterson and James M. Robinson, Chapter 3, http://gnosis.org/naghamm/gth_pat_rob.htm.

OVER TIME, and by trusting the mystery of it all, my life in Gallia seemed to lead me to where I needed to be. It led me to the people who needed me the most, and to those who were hungry to learn the power of God and be reunited with His divine love.

We created a strong affiliation with the community of our new village. Philip and I offered our healings and prayers in exchange for safe housing, food and protection. The more we worked with the locals, the more word of our work spread, and before we knew it we were hosting regular public meetings, similar to what Yeshua had started in Jerusalem. In a large cave overlooking the sacred beach where we had landed, we created our very own sacred Temple. There, surrounded by candlelight and the sweet sounds of the sea, we gathered and prayed together.

In that sacred Temple, while caring for my baby girl and holding her in my arms, I would tell the people about Yeshua and what he had taught us. I reconnected the people with the all-loving and mighty God, who lived within each and every one of us. I healed when I was called to heal and taught the daughters of the village our ancient practices, showing them how they too could heal the needy.

Every day, I lived my sacred teachings and rituals, all the while watching my daughter grow stronger and older. For her own protection, and ours, Philip and I had decided to never tell her who her father was. Although she would learn all about Yeshua, we decided that she would never know his true identity as her father. Instead, we told her that her father was a true follower of Yeshua and God who had died in the battles against the Roman soldiers while we were in exile.

Philip, living up to the promise he had made in Alexandria, spent his days forming an army. This army would protect all those who came to pray with us. They would protect our identity and, most importantly, our secret teachings. Although we had arrived in what seemed to be a safe place, we were still considered enemies of the Roman state and we knew that we could not afford to take any risks.

Philip also continued his writings, and in order to conserve his faith and dedication to his cause, he chose not to marry. He lived out the rest of his days as our personal protector and a strong male presence for Mary.

Sarah stayed on with us for a time and she too learnt the mysteries of healings and sacred female practices. Not after long, she married one of the soldiers who looked after us and started a beautiful family of her own.

Mary and Christopher stayed close to us in Arelate, and played an important part in spreading the word of Yeshua. Sadly, after only a few years in our new home, Mary fell terribly ill and passed away.

I often sent letters to Mary and Joseph, who remained in Bethlehem. I would send word of our new life and tell them all about Mary and how well she was doing. Joseph began to suffer from various health struggles, and in the third winter after our arrival, we received word that he'd passed on.

Mary came to visit us a few years after his death. It was wonderful to be with her and embrace her again. Though I begged her to stay, to live with us, she refused to stay long, telling us she had something stirring in her heart that she had to follow, so I trusted it was God's will. She had received word that Peter was in Rome and had started a strong following there, and she planned to travel to see him there. I sensed she had something important to share with him, but I did not insist on knowing more.

I did not hear from Mary after her departure, and I am unsure whether she ever made it to Rome. I do know in my heart that she lived a great life, and that wherever she spent her final days, they were filled with blessings, peace and joy.

Our life in Arelate was uneventful, happy and fruitful. Our new home brought us contentment and peace; lives that were continuously blessed with sun-filled days, fruitful crops and the constant company of our honest and humble neighbours. We lived in a true community, each of us helping whoever needed it the most. We lived in grace and gratitude for all that God had given us and all the eternal truths that Yeshua had opened our hearts and minds to.

I grew old in Arelate, and flourished by watching my daughter grow kind and wise, more brave than I could ever have become. She possessed a burning light inside of her that shone through her soul and lit up everyone she encountered.

She too fell in love and started a beautiful family of her own. She was a gracious mother, a natural healer who carried a deep inner knowing. She was my personal daily inspiration, and reminded me of Yeshua, possessing a charm and charisma that could captivate the attention and capture the hearts of the masses. It was evident that Yeshua lived boldly through her and I was so proud of the fine woman she had become.

Although I lost Yeshua too soon, his love and wisdom opened an entire new world for me. I remained in awe of him and of how strong his presence was felt within our daughter.

It was in Arelate that I lived out the rest of my days, in complete dedication and surrender to the glory of all that was and all that would ever be. I savoured every second I shared with my daughter and basked in her beauty. She was my rock, my teacher and the centre of my universe. My blood and the blood of Yeshua, combined for as long as she was alive, would run through her veins and the veins of her children, and their children, and their children, and so on for an eternity. We had created the first drop of a waterfall, which would grow, flow and flourish for lifetimes to come. Our waterfall would exist and burst with an inner knowledge of all that I and Yeshua represented; doubled in strength and more powerful than anything we could imagine.

These thoughts and profound realisations of what we had accomplished comforted me. I had become the priestess warrior who had already won each battle before they even began. Nothing could ever conquer the love Yeshua and I shared, nor tear it or us apart.

I was at peace with the world and at peace with all that we had achieved. His teachings were thriving all around us and I knew that when it was my time to go, he would be with me once again. I also knew that all the hard work we had done to establish a new home and to share his blessing in Gallia, would continue to flourish and thrive in my absence.

When the days started to get longer and my body heavier, I knew my time on this plane was approaching. My hair was long and gray, my muscles weak, my mind still and my heart full.

I spent the last forty days of my life in prayer. I sat in silence and listened to the eternal and universal love that radiated around me and continued to flow through my veins. I reflected on all that had passed and gave thanks for all I had received in my life.

When my body was approaching its last hours and moments, I peacefully surrendered it to the Lord. It was my time to leave this world and I looked forward to my soul being reborn.

I had honoured Yeshua in this life and was ready to reunite with him in the next.

I gave thanks for the opportunity to have experienced such a great love, though in my final moments, that love felt as if it had occurred a lifetime ago. But I had continued to love Yeshua with every single heartbeat of my life. I'd loved him with every cell of my being, right up to that sacred moment when my body took its final breath. With Mary holding my hand and Philip by my side, I smiled softly as my soul gently and gracefully departed my body.

As my spirit rose from my body, I was finally reunited with Yeshua. Surrounded in a beaming light and brimming with love, he came towards me and reached out his hand. I clasped onto it as we walked my final journey from this world into the next together. He guided and embraced me with such unconditional love and pride as we walked hand in hand into the heavens.

The Final Word

As long as this is hidden, unhappiness prevails; it always poisons the seeds, and evil is at work. But when it is manifest, the clear light will envelop all, and everyone who finds themselves in it will be anointed. Slaves and prisoners will be freed.

126: If a plant has not been planted by my Father who is in heaven, it will be uprooted. Those who were separated will reunite and become fertilized. All those who practice the sacred embrace will kindle the light; they will not beget as people do in ordinary marriages, which take place in darkness. The fire that burns by night flares up, and then is gone; but the mystery of that embrace is never extinguished; it happens in that light of day which knows no sunset.

127: If someone experiences Trust and Consciousness in the heart of the embrace, they become a child of light. If someone does not receive these, it is because they remain attached to what they know; when they cease to be attached, they will be able to receive them. Whoever receives this light in nakedness will no longer be recognizable; none will be able to grasp them, none will be able to make them sad or miserable, whether they are in this world, or have left it. They already know the truth in images. For them, this world has become another world, and this Temple Space is fullness. They are who they are. Neither shadow nor night can hide them.[20]

— THE GOSPEL OF PHILIP

20 The Gospel of Philip, Page 87, Plate 133, Translated by Jean-Yves Leloup, Inner Traditions 2004, p.171-173.

THE END

BIBLIOGRAPHY

Books

The Gospel of Philip: Jesus, Mary Magdalene, and the Gnosis
of Sacred Union, by Jean-Yves Leloup, Inner Traditions
2004

The Fifth Gospel: The Gospel of Thomas Comes of Age,
Translated by Stephen J. Patterson, James M. Robinson,
Hans-Gebhard Bethge, Trinity Press International 1998

The Nag Hammadi Scriptures: The Revised and Updated
Translation of Sacred Gnostic Texts Complete in One
Volume, edited by Marvin W Meyer, HarperOne 2009

The Gospel of Mary of Magdala: Jesus and the First Woman
Apostle, by Karen L King, Polebridge Press 2003

Introduction to the Synoptic Gospels by Pheme Perkins, Wm.
B. Eerdmans Publishing 2009

The Sacred Embrace of Jesus and Mary: The Sexual Mystery at
the Heart of the Christian Tradition by Jean-Yves Leloup,
Inner Traditions 2006

About the Author

Bridget Erica is an internationally sought-after Usui Reiki Master, teacher and healer, self-proclaimed early Christian investigator, and writer. Her passion for energy healing, combined with her personal pursuit to uncover hidden stories from the past, inspired her to re-write the story of Mary Magdalene, one of the most misunderstood and influential women and healers in history. Bridget resides in Rome with her husband and two children. Magdala is her first novel.

Bridget is the founder of the Australian Centre for Clinical Reiki and creator of several self-healing courses. She provides personal healing sessions to people from all over the world. You can learn more about her courses and offerings at www.bridgeterica.com or www.thereikitemple.com

About the Artist

Jennifer Taranto is the artist behind the beautiful cover image of Mary Magdalene. Jennifer was born in Melbourne in 1957 and first discovered her passion for painting at the tender age of eight.

Over the past 40 years Jennifer has had a long successful career as an artist, including creating illustrations for screen printing; illustrating children's and botanical books; and exhibiting her work at numerous solo shows across Australia.

Working in all mediums, Jennifer's subject matter ranges from botanical to landscape, and abstract to illustration (of Australian Wildlife). She also designs for clothing and commercial products.

Her works are sold nationally and internationally. You can get in touch with Jennifer and view her work at www.jataranto.com.au